Workbook

Spanish

False beginners

Belén Ausejo – Juan Córdoba

Adapted for English speakers
by Paul Gerard Pickering

About this workbook

The 16 lessons in this workbook, which contain some 170 exercises, will allow you to progressively review and practice the fundamentals of Castilian Spanish (i.e. the Spanish spoken in Spain), from pronunciation and vocabulary through to simple and more complex sentence construction.

One of the trickier aspects of Spanish is the conjugation and usage of verb tenses. As a result, this is given particular emphasis in this workbook. The verb conjugation tables at the end give both regular and common irregular conjugations.

To complement the exercises, three sections devoted to vocabulary and reading comprehension are interspersed among the lessons. These allow active and contextual reinforcement of new words and expressions. We hope you will find that this workbook provides a fun and systematic way to consolidate your Spanish skills.

As you work through the lessons, you can self-assess your results by selecting the appropriate icon after each exercise (☺ if the majority of your answers were correct, ☹ if half your answers were correct, or ☹ if less than half were correct). After a lesson, enter the number of icons of each type you received in the exercises, and then enter these totals into the final score table at the end of the workbook so you can tally your overall score after completing all the exercises.

Contents

Letters, sounds & punctuation

Alphabet and pronunciation

- The Spanish alphabet contains 27 letters, one more than in the English alphabet. The extra letter is **ñ**, which corresponds to the sound [ny], as in *canyon*.

a (a)	f (efe)	k (ka)	o (o)	t (te)	y (i griega)
b (be)	g (ge)	l (ele)	p (pe)	u (u)	z (zeta)
c (ce)	h (hache)	m (eme)	q (cu)	v (uve)	
d (de)	i (i)	n (ene)	r (erre)	w (uve doble)	
e (e)	j (jota)	ñ (eñe)	s (ese)	x (equis)	

- On the whole, Spanish words are pronounced very much as they are written. Here are the main pronunciation differences with English:

  - **a** is pronounced like the [ah] in *father*
  - **e** is pronounced like the [ay] in *they* or the [e] in *bet;* **i** is like the [ee] in *bee*
  - **o** is pronounced like the [o] in *no;* **u** is like the [oo] in *food*
  - **c** is pronounced as [k] in **ca, co, cu**, but as [th] in **ce** and **ci**
  - **g** is pronounced as a hard [g] in **ga, go, gu,** but like the Spanish **j** in **ge** and **gi**
  - **h** is always silent
  - **j (la jota)** is a guttural [kh] as in the Scottish word *loch*
  - **ll** is pronounced more or less like the [y] in *yes*
  - **r** is rolled, by trilling the tip of the tongue against the roof of the mouth
  - **v** is pronounced almost like a [b]
  - **z** is pronounced like the [th] in *think*

> Acronyms are quite common in Spanish. Have a look at the names of the letters above and then write the acronyms for the terms below followed by the letter names (as if you were pronouncing them out loud). E.g. Compact Disc: CD (ce de)

a. Disco Versátil Digital: ....

b. Global Positioning System: ....

c. Documento Nacional de Identidad: ....

d. World Wide Web: ....

e. Organización No Gubernamental: ....

f. HyperText Transfer Protocol: ....

2 After reviewing the rules on page 3, put each of the following words into the table below according to the pronunciation of its first letter. Try to do it without looking back at the rules!

calor *heat*
camino *path*
cero *zero*
ciruela *plum*
colega *colleague*
cumpleaños *birthday*
gafas *glasses/ spectacles*
gato *cat*
gel *gel*
girasol *sunflower*
gitano *gypsy*
golondrina *swallow* (bird)

gorra *cap*
guerra *war*
guitarra *guitar*
hasta *until*
hay *there is/are*
helado *ice cream*

hija *daughter*
hola *hello*
huevo *egg*
jamón *ham*
jirafa *giraffe*
julio *July*

queso *cheese*
quizás *perhaps*
zapato *shoe*
zoológico *zoo*
zorro *fox*
zumo *juice*

SILENT	LIKE [TH] IN ENGLISH	LIKE THE SPANISH JOTA	LIKE A HARD [G] IN ENGLISH	LIKE [K] IN ENGLISH

Word stress

- To avoid sounding like a **guiri** *foreign tourist*, try to accentuate the right syllable in words – it's fairly straightforward in Spanish!

- In words ending in a vowel, an **-n** or an **-s**, the next-to-last syllable is stressed when speaking: **España**, **Carmen**, **Honduras**.

- In words ending in a consonant other than **-n** or **-s** the final syllable is stressed: **Madrid**, **amor**, **abril**.

- If a written accent appears over a vowel (which is the case if there is an exception to these rules), that syllable is stressed: **Panamá**, **crédito**, **agitación**.

3 As in the example (Francia), indicate where the stress falls in the name of each country by ticking the corresponding column: the orange bar at the top indicates which syllable is stressed.

	▮▯	▯▮▯	▯▯▮	▯▮	▮▯
a. Francia					✔
b. México					
c. España					
d. Portugal					
e. Perú					
f. Bélgica					
g. Canadá					
h. Holanda					
i. Suiza					
j. Brasil					

4 The words below follow the normal rules for where the stress falls. Mark the syllable where each word should be stressed.

a. paella ▢▢▢   **e.** mujer ▢▢   **i.** estadio ▢▢▢

b. gambas ▢▢   **f.** salud ▢▢   **j.** pasaporte ▢▢▢▢

c. arroz ▢▢   **g.** voleibol ▢▢▢   **k.** Valladolid ▢▢▢▢

d. cerveza ▢▢▢   **h.** Esteban ▢▢▢   **l.** martes ▢▢

5 The following words are exceptions to the normal rules for word stress. Rewrite each word, placing an accent on the vowel where the stress falls.

a. frances ....

b. Cadiz ....

c. futbol ....

d. cafe ....

e. Paris ....

f. dolar ....

g. menu ....

h. sofa ....

i. sandwich ....

j. modem ....

k. vater ....

l. jamon ....

Word stress 2

• **A spelling tip**

Typically, a word's <u>spoken</u> stress remains the same even if the word is changed – for example, if a syllable is added to form the plural. But although the spoken stress does not change, a <u>written</u> accent may either appear or disappear:

• **un inglés** *an Englishman*, but **dos ingleses** *two Englishmen* (the written accent disappears in the plural)

• **un joven** *a young man*, but **dos jóvenes** *two young men* (a written accent appears in the plural)

6 Add a written accent to the plural forms if necessary.

a. **un árbol** *a tree* ➜ **dos arboles**

b. **un inglés** *an Englishman* ➜ **dos ingleses**

c. **un balón** *a ball* ➜ **dos balones**

d. **un andén** *a platform* ➜ **dos andenes**

e. **un móvil** *a mobile phone* ➜ **dos moviles**

7 Add a written accent to the singular forms if necessary.

a. **dos alemanes** *two Germans* ➜ **un aleman**

b. **dos portátiles** *two laptops* ➜ **un portatil**

c. **dos papeles** *two papers* ➜ **un papel**

d. **dos daneses** *two Danes* ➜ **un danes**

e. **dos mítines** *two meetings* ➜ **un mitin**

Punctuation

- In Spanish, exclamation marks (**los signos de admiración**) and question marks (**los signos de interrogación**) come at the beginning and end of a sentence: the one at the beginning of the sentence is upside down: ¡...! ¿...?

- When using the Internet, you may need to know the names of various punctuation marks: **el punto** *dot, full stop, period*; **dos puntos** *colon*; **el guión** *hyphen, dash*; **el guión bajo** *underscore*; **la barra** *forward slash*; **la barra doble** *double forward slash*, and last but not least, **la arroba**, the name of the @ symbol.

8 Question or exclamation? Punctuate the bubbles!

e. HOLA

f. CÓMO TE LLAMAS

d. DE DÓNDE ERES

c. BIENVENIDO

b. HABLAS ESPAÑOL

a. ENCANTADO

9 Write these Internet addresses as if you were saying them out loud, including the name of each type of punctuation.

a. http://www.assimil.com/

→ ....

b. belen_ausejo@hotmail.com

→ ....

c. juan-cordoba@gmail.com

→ ....

Well done! You've reached the end of Lesson 1. It's time to count up how many of each type of icon you received. Then record your results in the final self-assessment table on page 128.

Articles, nouns, adjectives & numbers

Articles and nouns

- Spanish has four forms of the definite article (*the*), which depend on a noun's gender and number: **el** (masculine singular), **la** (feminine singular), **los** (masculine plural) and **las** (feminine plural). Certain articles contract after certain prepositions:
  a + el → al *to the*   **de + el → del** *of the*

Note: Only the singular articles contract, never the plural.

- To form the plural of nouns (and most adjectives), **-s** is added to words ending in a vowel, and **-es** to words ending in a consonant or a **-y**:

  el hombre alto *the tall man* → **los hombres altos** *the tall men*
  la mujer actual *the modern woman* → **las mujeres actuales** *the modern women*
  la ley nacional *the national law* → **las leyes nacionales** *the national laws*

Note: Unlike in English, descriptive adjectives usually follow the noun in Spanish.

- There are two forms of singular indefinite article (*a/an*): **un huevo** *an egg* (masculine), **una manzana** *an apple* (feminine).

- The plural indefinite article (*some/any*) is usually omitted when talking about something generally. Otherwise, **unos** (masculine), **unas** (feminine) can be used:

  ¿Hay manzanas? → *Are there any apples?*
  Quiero pan. → *I want some bread.*
  Tengo unos calcetines nuevos. → *I have some new socks.*

 Here are the titles of six famous films with the articles (or contracted article + preposition) missing. Insert the articles on the clapperboard into the correct places in the film titles.

a. Mujeres .... borde de un ataque de nervios

b. .... cabaña .... tío Tom

c. .... señor .... anillos

d. .... guerra .... galaxias

e. Blancanieves y .... siete enanitos

f. .... libro .... selva

2 Fill in the blanks to complete these phrases in Spanish.

a. The price of the Spanish omelette.
El precio ....

b. I want some Spanish omelette.
Quiero ....

c. I want a Spanish omelette.
Quiero ....

d. I want some apples.
Quiero ....

e. The price of the eggs.
El precio ....

f. I want some eggs.
Quiero ....

g. I want some wine.
Quiero ....

h. I want a [loaf of] bread.
Quiero ....

3 Put these noun phrases into the singular.

a. Los productos de los mercados → ....

b. Las imágenes de las ciudades → ....

c. Las leyes de los países → ....

Masculine and feminine

- In general, most nouns ending in **-o** are masculine, and most ending in **-a** are feminine. However, there are exceptions, some of which are frequently used words: **la mano** *hand*; **la modelo** *fashion model*; **el día** *day*; **el idioma** *language*; **el problema** *problem*, etc.

- Nouns ending in **-ista** and **-ante** are the same for both genders: **el/la cantante** *the singer* (m./f.); **el/la deportista** *the athlete* (m./f.).

- When describing people, masculine nouns ending in **-o** change to **-a** in the feminine: **el hijo** *son*, **la hija** *daughter*. Those ending in **-or** change to **-ora** in the feminine: **el profesor / la profesora** *the teacher* (m./f.).

- Adjectives ending in **-o** change to **-a** in the feminine, but if they end in any other vowel or a consonant, the ending doesn't change for gender: **un chico alegre** *a happy boy*; **una chica alegre** *a happy girl*.

9

4 Complete the following table with the correct forms for gender and number.

FEMININE SINGULAR	MASCULINE SINGULAR	FEMININE PLURAL	MASCULINE PLURAL
	el estudiante serio		
la directora alegre			
		las tenistas tristes	
			los chicos simpáticos
la pianista famosa			
	el escritor interesante		
			los amigos fieles
		las cantantes actuales	

5 Complete these phrases with the right colour, making sure the adjective agrees with the noun in gender and number.

a. La sangre es ....

b. Los troncos de los árboles son ....

c. La leche es ....

d. Tus ojos son .... como el cielo.

e. La hierba es ....

f. Las panteras son ....

g. El jamón de york es ....

h. Los limones son ....

blanco

negro

rojo

rosa

amarillo

verde

marrón

azul

Adjectives of nationality

- Adjectives describing nationality that end in **-o** in the masculine take **-a** in the feminine. If they end in any other vowel, the ending doesn't change for gender.
  norteamericano / norteamericana *North American* (m./f.)
  croata *Croatian* (m./f.)
  canadiense *Canadian* (m./f.)
  israelí *Israeli* (m./f.)

- If the adjective ends in a consonant in the masculine, the feminine is formed by adding an **-a** ending (and dropping the written accent):
  inglés / inglesa *English* (m./f.)

- To give your nationality, use the verb **ser** + adjective: **Soy irlandés.** *I* (m.) *am Irish.* To say what city you are from, use **ser de** + city. **Es de Londres.** *He's from London.*

6 Use these 18 labels (6 names, 6 nationalities and 6 cities) to form six pairs of sentences by combining a name, nationality (make sure the gender agrees) and city. E.g. Inés es española. Es de Barcelona.

alemán   marroquí   Fernanda   estadounidense   Rabat   Inge

Barack   Berlín   belga   Guadalupe   portugués   mexicano

Cancún   Jacques   Bruselas   Nueva York   Samia   Lisboa

a. Barack es .... Es de ....

b. Jacques es .... Es de ....

c. Samia es .... Es de ....

d. Fernanda es .... Es de ....

e. Inge es .... Es de ....

f. Guadalupe es .... Es de ....

Numbers

- The numbers from 0 to 29 are written as a single word. From 30 on, the tens and units are written as separate words, with a **y** *and* in the middle.

0 cero	10 diez	20 veinte	30 treinta
1 uno	11 once	21 veintiuno	31 treinta y uno
2 dos	12 doce	22 veintidós	32 treinta y dos, etc.
3 tres	13 trece	23 veintitrés	40 cuarenta
4 cuatro	14 catorce	24 veinticuatro	50 cincuenta
5 cinco	15 quince	25 veinticinco	60 sesenta
6 seis	16 dieciséis	26 veintiséis	70 setenta
7 siete	17 diecisiete	27 veintisiete	80 ochenta
8 ocho	18 dieciocho	28 veintiocho	90 noventa
9 nueve	19 diecinueve	29 veintinueve	100 cien

- From 101 to 199, **cien** becomes **ciento** (**ciento uno, ciento dos** up to **ciento noventa y nueve**). It remains **cien** when used as a multiple of a number (**cien mil, cien millones**).

- From 200 on, hundreds are considered as adjectives and must agree in gender: **doscien<u>tos</u> amig<u>os</u>, trescien<u>tas</u> cincuenta amig<u>as</u>**.

100 cien, ciento	600 seiscientos/-as
200 doscientos/-as	700 setecientos/-as
300 trescientos/-as	800 ochocientos/-as
400 cuatrocientos/-as	900 novecientos/-as
500 quinientos/-as	1000 mil, 2000 dos mil, etc.

7 Write out the equations on the blackboard in Spanish (as words), as well as their results: *más* (·), *menos* (−), *por* (x), *entre* (÷), *igual* (=).

a. ....

....

b. ....

....

c. ....

....

d. ....

....

$$7 \times 11 =$$
$$33 - 8 =$$
$$14 + 15 =$$
$$84 \div 4 =$$

8 Which boxes must you go through in order to get out of this maze? Write out the numbers of your path as words.

a. ....

b. ....

c. ....

d. ....

e. ....

f. ....

g. ....

h. ....

i. ....

j. ....

k. ....

l. ....

m. ....

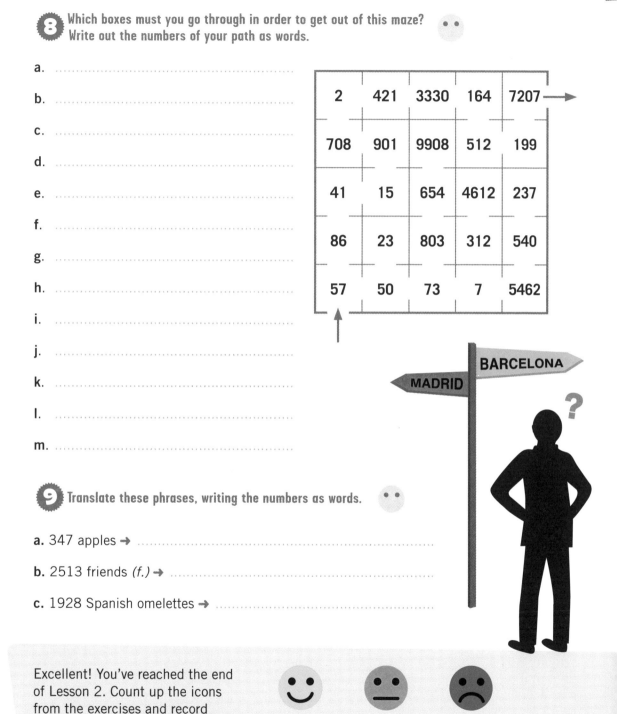

2	421	3330	164	7207
708	901	9908	512	199
41	15	654	4612	237
86	23	803	312	540
57	50	73	7	5462

BARCELONA

MADRID

9 Translate these phrases, writing the numbers as words.

a. 347 apples → ....

b. 2513 friends *(f.)* → ....

c. 1928 Spanish omelettes → ....

Excellent! You've reached the end of Lesson 2. Count up the icons from the exercises and record your result in the final evaluation table on page 128.

Conjugation & personal pronouns

Regular verbs in the present tense

- There are three groups of Spanish verbs, which conjugate in slightly different ways: those with infinitives ending in **-ar**, **-er** and **-ir** (see conjugation tables, pp. 114–115).

- Because the conjugation endings for each person are different, the subject pronoun is used only for emphasis or clarification: **canto** *I sing*, but **yo canto** *I sing* (as opposed to someone else); **canta** *he sings*, but **él canta** <u>*he*</u> *sings.*

<u>Subject pronouns</u>
yo *I*
tú *you* (sing. informal)
él / ella *he, it* (m.) / *she, it* (f.)
nosotros/-as *we* (m./f.)
vosotros/-as *you* (pl. informal)
ellos / ellas *they* (m./f.)

<u>Note:</u> There are different forms for *you* in Spanish: more on this later!

I Conjugate these verbs in the right person and then put them into the correct place in the crossword. The first letter of one of the verbs has been given. The verbs are: *hablar* (to speak, to talk), *cantar* (to sing), *bailar* (to dance), *comer* (to eat), *beber* (to drink), *leer* (to read), *vivir* (to live), *escribir* (to write), *abrir* (to open).

a. You read *(pl. informal)* ....

b. We sing ....

c. He writes ....

d. I speak ....

e. I open ....

f. We dance ....

g. They read ....

h. You eat *(sing. informal)* ....

i. You drink *(pl. informal)* ....

j. We live ....

2 Find 10 present tense verb forms in this *sopa de letras* (alphabet soup) and then list and translate them below. The verbs might appear horizontally, vertically or diagonally.

a. .... → ....

b. .... → ....

c. .... → ....

d. .... → ....

e. .... → ....

f. .... → ....

g. .... → ....

h. .... → ....

i. .... → ....

j. .... → ....

B	A	I	L	O	U	T	X	E	I
E	R	T	A	L	H	A	B	L	E
B	O	L	L	Y	A	V	I	V	E
E	S	C	R	I	B	Í	S	T	O
M	U	A	C	H	L	O	L	O	T
O	C	N	T	O	A	B	R	E	S
S	O	T	I	U	M	B	C	H	E
O	M	A	N	G	O	E	L	F	P
T	A	N	X	Y	S	V	N	A	R

Object pronouns

- Personal pronouns can have different forms depending on if they are the subject (e.g. *I*, *he*, etc.) or the object (e.g. *me*, *him*, etc.) of the verb. In Spanish, the third-person object pronouns also differ depending on if they are direct (*I see him*) or indirect (*I give it to him*). Object pronouns generally come <u>before</u> the verb:
  Lo veo. *I see <u>him</u>.*

- Referring to a third person, you might hear either **le** or **lo** used as the direct object (but only in the masculine): **Le/Lo quiero mucho.** *I like him very much.*

Direct objects	Indirect objects
me *me*	**me**
te *you* (sing. informal)	**te**
lo (le) / la *him/her/it*	**le (se)**
nos *us*	**nos**
os *you* (pl. informal)	**os**
los / las *them* (m./f.)	**les (se)**

- If a direct and indirect object are used together, the indirect object comes first. In the third person, **le** and **les** change to **se** in this case.
  Se lo digo. *I tell it to him/them.*
  ↑ ↑   ↑   ↑
  IO DO   DO IO

3 Replace the words in italics in the sentences below with the corresponding direct object. E.g. I read *books*. ➜ I read them.

a. Leo *libros*.

.... leo.

b. Compro *pan*.

....compro.

c. Como *huevos*.

....como.

d. Toco *la guitarra*.

.... toco.

e. Quiero *tortillas*.

.... quiero.

f. Canto *las canciones*.

.... canto.

g. Escribo *una carta*.

.... escribo.

h. Hablo *español*.

.... hablo.

HABLO ESPAÑOL

4 Translate each sentence and then rewrite it, replacing the noun or noun phrase in italics with the corresponding direct object pronoun.

He writes us *letters*.

a. .... cartas.

b. ....

We write you (pl. inf.) *an e-mail*.

c. .... un mail.

d. ....

You (sing. inf.) read *books* to me.

e. .... libros.

f. ....

They open *their arms* to you (sing. inf.).

g. .... los brazos.

h. ....

We open *the door* for them.

i. .... la puerta.

j. ....

I read *poems* to him.

k. .... poesías.

l. ....

Pronouns used after a preposition

- Typically, object pronouns come before the verb in Spanish: **Le hablo.** *I speak to him.* However, they can also be used after a preposition, in which case the subject pronouns are usually used: **Hablo con él.** *I speak with him.* **Esto es para ellos.** *This is for them.*

- The two exceptions are **mí** and **ti**, which are used after all prepositions apart from **con**. With this preposition, the first two persons have special forms: **conmigo** *with me* and **contigo** *with you*.

- The preposition **a** is required before a direct object that designates a person: **Veo a una mujer.** *I see a woman.*

a *to*	
de *of, for*	
por *through, for*	**mí**
para *for*	**ti**
en *in, on*	**él/ella**
sin *without*	**nosotros/-as**
delante de *in front of*	**vosotros/-as**
detrás de *behind*	**ellos/ellas**
antes de *before*	
después de *after*	

5 Translate these sentences.

a. The book is for them *(f.)*.

→ ....

b. You *(sing. inf.)* sing with me.

→ ....

c. We dance in front of them *(m.)*.

→ ....

d. You *(pl. inf.)* eat after us.

→ ....

e. I visit my friends.

→ ....

f. I eat without you *(sing. inf)*.

→ ....

g. He wants to eat with you *(sing. inf)*.

→ ....

6 Rewrite the sentences below using one of the following prepositions: *delante de / antes de / después de / detrás de.*

a. Me lavo las manos XXX comer.

→ ....

b. Me lavo los dientes XXX comer.

→ ....

c. Como XXX la tele.

→ ....

d. Echo la siesta XXX comer.

→ ....

e. Se esconde XXX un árbol.

→ ....

Saying 'to like'

- To say you want or would like something, use **querer** *to want*: **Quiero pan.** *I'd like some bread.* (Note that this verb is also used to express love for someone: **Te quiero.** *I love you.*)

- To say you like something, **gustar** is used, which more directly translates as *to appeal to*. **Me gusta el libro.** *I like the book.* ('To me appeals the book'). This is why the verb conjugates according to what is appealing (so in the singular or plural) and the person who 'likes' is an object pronoun.

  Me gustan los libros. *I like the books.* ('To me they appeal the books.')
  Nos gusta el libro. *We like the book.* ('To us it appeals the book.')

- Two other verbs that express likes and dislikes conjugate in a similar way:
  me horroriza(n) *I hate* (sing./pl.) and **me encanta(n)** *I love/adore* (sing./pl.).

- To add emphasis, the preposition **a** + pronoun is used: **A mí me gusta comer.** *As for me, I like to eat.* To say you don't like something, just add **no**:
  No me gusta. *I don't like it.*

7 Use the boxes marked in the table below to write six sentences in Spanish.
E.g. (box 1): A ellos les encanta España.

	España	las gambas	los ordenadores	leer libros
ellos	♥ ♥		💥	
nosotras		♥		
yo			💥 💥	
tú		♥ ♥		
vosotros	♥			
él				💥

♥ = gustar

♥ ♥ = encantar

💥 = no gustar

💥 💥 = horrorizar

a. ....

b. ....

c. ....

d. ....

e. ....

f. ....

The different forms of *you*

- Spanish has different ways to say *you* depending on who is being addressed. In many cases, the informal *you* is used: **tú** for one person (second-person singular) or **vosotros/-as** for more than one person (second-person plural).

- But in formal contexts or to show respect for older people or superiors, politeness is expressed with **usted** for one person (third-person singular) or **ustedes** for more than one person (third-person plural). The formal *you* always conjugates in the third person: **¿Quiere usted tortilla?** *Do you want some Spanish omelette?*

- The third-person object pronouns are also used for the formal *you*: **¿Le gusta España?** *Do you like Spain?* (formal). Basically, in formal or particularly polite contexts, the person or group you are speaking to should be addressed in the third person. (Note that this means that the third person in Spanish can translate in several ways: **¿Es español?** *Is he Spanish? Is she Spanish? Are you Spanish?*)

8 Rewrite this conversation in the bubbles on the right, using the polite form of *you*.

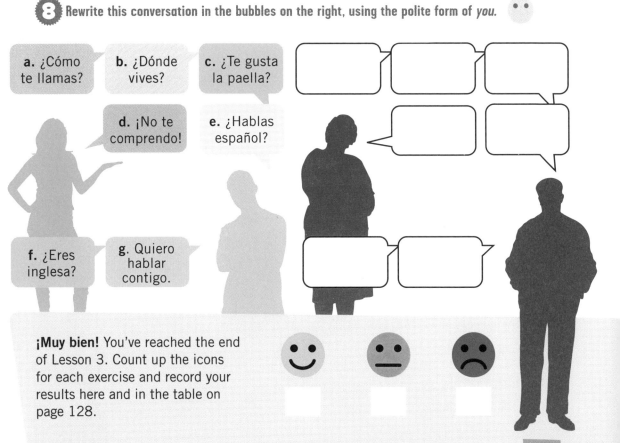

a. ¿Cómo te llamas?

b. ¿Dónde vives?

c. ¿Te gusta la paella?

d. ¡No te comprendo!

e. ¿Hablas español?

f. ¿Eres inglesa?

g. Quiero hablar contigo.

¡Muy bien! You've reached the end of Lesson 3. Count up the icons for each exercise and record your results here and in the table on page 128.

Possessives, demonstratives & indefinite pronour

Possessive adjectives and pronouns

- In Spanish, possessive adjectives (*my, your, his, her, its, our, their*) and pronouns (*mine, yours, his, hers, ours, theirs*) have to agree in gender and number with the noun they refer to:

  nuestro(s) hermano(s) *our brother(s)*
  nuestra(s) hermana(s) *our sister(s)*

  - The third-person **su** (used with singular nouns) or **sus** (used with plural nouns) can mean *his, her, its, your* (formal) or *their*.

  - The possessive pronoun is usually preceded by the definite article: **Es el mío.** *It's mine.*

Adjective	Pronoun
mi(s)	el (los) mío(s), la(s) mía(s)
tu(s)	el (los) tuyo(s), la(s) tuya(s)
su(s)	el (los) suyo(s), la(s) suya(s)
nuestro(s), nuestra(s)	el (los) nuestro(s), la(s) nuestra(s)
vuestro(s), vuestra(s)	el (los) vuestro(s), la(s) vuestra(s)
su(s)	el (los) suyo(s), la(s) suya(s)

1 Complete these sentences using the appropriate possessive adjective.

a. Tengo dos cartas. → Son .... cartas.

b. Tenemos un pasaporte. → Es .... pasaporte.

c. Tenéis tres guitarras. → ....

d. Tienen diez móviles. → ....

e. Tiene muchos colegas. → ....

f. Tenéis un libro. → ....

g. Tienes un perro. → ....

h. Tienes dos profesores. → ....

i. Tenemos dos guitarras. → ....

j. Tiene un portátil. → ....

k. Tengo un amigo. → ....

l. Tienen un balón. → ....

2 Finish each sentence with the appropriate possessive pronoun.

a. No es mi libro, es tu libro. → No es mi libro, es el ....

b. No son mis gafas, son tus gafas. → No son mis gafas, son ....

c. No son mis amigos, son tus amigos. → No son mis amigos, son ....

d. No es tu carta, es mi carta. → No es tu carta, es ....

e. No es tu abuela, es su abuela. → No es tu abuela, es ....

f. No son mis primas, son sus primas. → No son mis primas, son ....

g. No es tu padre, es su padre. → No es tu padre, es ....

h. No es su ordenador, es mi ordenador. → No es su ordenador, es ....

i. No son sus discos, son mis discos. → No son sus discos, son ....

'It's mine, it's his', etc.

- To show possession with the verb **ser** *to be*, the possessive pronoun is often used without the article:

  El libro es mío. *The book is mine.*
  Las gafas son tuyas. *The glasses are yours* (sing. inf.).
  El perro es suyo. *The dog is his / hers / yours* (formal) / *theirs.*
  La casa es vuestra. *The house is yours* (pl. inf.).

- In the third person, **es** + **de** *of* + name or pronoun can also be used to show possession:

  Es de Pedro. *It's Pedro's.*
  Es de ellas. *It's theirs* (f.).

3 Translate these sentences.

a. The dog *(f.)* isn't ours.

→ ....

b. The laptop is mine.

→ ....

c. The books are theirs. *(2 possibilities)*

→ ....

→ ....

d. The guitar isn't yours *(sing. inf.)*.

→ ....

e. The apples aren't yours *(pl. inf.)*.

→ ....

f. The discs aren't yours *(sing. inf.)*.

→ ....

The different forms of *your/yours*

- When using the informal **tú** (second-person singular), the possessive adjective is **tu** (with a singular noun) / **tus** (with a plural noun):

  Es tu amigo. *He's your friend.* **Son tus amigos.** *They are your friends.*

- When using the formal **usted** (third-person singular), the possessive adjective is **su** (with a singular noun) / **sus** (with a plural noun):

  Es su amigo, señor. *He is your friend, sir.*
  (But remember that **su/sus** can also mean *his*, *her*, *its*, *their*.)

- In the plural, **vuestro/-a/-os/-as** is used for informally referring to more than one person, and **su/sus** is used for formally referring to more than one person.

  Es vuestra casa. *It's your house.* (pl. informal)
  Es su casa. *It's your house.* (pl. formal)

4 Tick which form of address is appropriate in each situation, then indicate possession in two ways as shown in the example.
E.g. Is it <u>your</u> beer? Is the beer <u>yours</u>?

Hablo con un colega: tratamiento de tú ☐   tratamiento de usted ☐

a. ¿Es .... cerveza?   ¿Es .... la cerveza?

b. ¿Son .... gambas?   ¿Son .... las gambas?

c. ¿Son .... discos?   ¿Son .... los discos?

d. ¿Es .... móvil?   ¿Es .... el móvil?

Hablo con mis hermanos: tratamiento de tú ☐   tratamiento de usted ☐

e. ¿Es .... libro?   ¿Es .... el libro?

f. ¿Es .... consola?   ¿Es .... la consola?

g. ¿Son .... patines?   ¿Son .... los patines?

h. ¿Son .... camisetas?   ¿Son .... las camisetas?

Hablo con la abuela de un amigo: tratamiento de tú ◯   tratamiento de usted ◯

i. ¿Es .... té?   ¿Es .... el té?

j. ¿Es .... revista?   ¿Es .... la revista?

k. ¿Son .... zapatos?   ¿Son .... los zapatos?

l. ¿Son .... gafas?   ¿Son .... las gafas?

Indefinite pronouns

Indefinite pronouns are used to refer to something vague without naming it specifically. Some common indefinite pronouns are:

- **algo** *something*; **nada** *nothing*
  Hay algo. *There is something.* **No hay nada.** *There isn't anything.*

  Nada can also mean *not at all*, and **algo** *a bit*, *somewhat*, *rather*.
  No me gusta nada. *I don't like it at all.* **Es algo serio.** *It's rather serious.*

- **alguien** *someone*; **nadie** *no one*
  With **nadie**, if used after the verb, the negative **no** needs to come before the verb (double negatives are grammatically acceptable in Spanish):
  Nadie canta. / No canta nadie. *No one is singing.*

  Since they refer to people, **alguien** and **nadie** are preceded by the preposition **a** when used as a direct object:
  No quiere a nadie. *He doesn't love anyone.* **Quiero a alguien.** *I love someone.*

5 Complete each sentence with *nada* or *nadie* and then translate it.

a. No comprendo ....

b. Aquí .... canta.

c. No quiero ....

d. .... me comprende.

e. No comprendo a ....

f. No es .... simpático.

g. Aquí no vive ....

h. .... me quiere.

6 Complete each sentence with *algo* or *alguien* and then translate it.

a. ¿Comprendes ....?

....

b. ¿A .... no le gusta la paella?

....

c. ¿Quieres beber ....?

....

d. ¿Quieres ....?

....

e. Quiero hablar con ....

....

f. ¡ .... te llama por teléfono!

....

g. ¿Vive .... aquí?

....

h. Hablo .... de inglés.

....

Demonstratives: 'this' and 'that'

- Demonstrative adjectives help to indicate distance from the speaker:

  Este libro, aquí. *This book here.*
  Esas bicicletas, ahí. *Those bikes there.*
  Aquel libro, allí. *That book over there.*

- The same forms are used for the pronouns, e.g.:

  este *this (one)*
  aquellos *those (ones)*

- The forms need to agree in gender and number with the noun they refer to:

  Este libro es mío.
  Esas bolsas son mías.

- **aquel** can also be used to indicate distance in time:

  En aquel tiempo.

		Near the speaker	Farther from the speaker	Even farther from the speaker
	Adverbs of place	**aquí** *here*	**ahí** *there*	**allí, allá** *over there*
	Demonstrative adjectives & pronouns	**este** *this* **estos** **esta** **estas**	**ese** *that* **esos** **esa** **esas**	**aquel** *that over there* **aquellos** **aquella** **aquellas**
	Neuter demonstratives (for abstract concepts)	**esto** *this*	**eso** *that*	**aquello** *that over there*

7 Complete these sentences with the appropriate adverbs of place. ●●

a. Me gusta bañarme .... , en esta playa.

b. Aquella playa, ... , es muy peligrosa.

c. ¿Qué es eso que llevas ....?

d. ¿Comemos .... , en este restaurante?

e. ¿Qué es aquello que veo.....................?

f. Escribe tu número .... , en esa libreta.

8 Now translate the sentences. ●●

a. ....
....

b. ....
....

c. ....
....

d. ....
....

e. ....
....

f. ....
....

9 Complete these sentences with the appropriate demonstrative adjectives. ●●

a. ¿Es tuyo ....bolígrafo, ahí en tu mesa?

b. Quiero .... manzanas, aquí, las rojas.

c. En .... tiempos, no existían los ordenadores.

d. Yo vivo aquí, en .... casa azul.

e. Mi abuelo vive allí, en .... casa verde.

f. ¿Son vuestros .... zapatos, ahí en el suelo?

Great work! You've reached the end of Lesson 4. Now count up the icons for each exercise and record your results here and in the table on page 128.

25

5

Ser, estar & progressive tenses

Two verbs for 'to be'

- There are two ways to expess *to be* in Spanish: **ser** and **estar**.

- **ser** is used to describe essential, inherent characteristics that are independent of the immediate circumstances of the subject. Thus, when making a statement about a noun, **ser** is used: **Es una casa.** *It's a house.* **Es profesor.** *He's a teacher.* So the issue of whether to use **ser** or **estar** mainly arises before an adjective.

- **estar** is used to describe a state or condition of something in time or space, i.e. things bound by circumstances (location, health, mood, etc.): **¿Dónde está el niño?** *Where is the boy?*

SER	ESTAR
soy	estoy
eres	estás
es	está
somos	estamos
sois	estáis
son	están

- So if an adjective defines an essential characteristic of identity (e.g. nationality, convictions, physical description), **ser** is used: **Es francés.** *He is French.* If the adjective refers to a temporary circumstance (e.g. state of mind, physical condition), the verb **estar** is used: **Está triste.** *He is sad.*

I Complete these sentences using the correct form of *ser* or *estar*.

a. I am Spanish.

→ .... española.

b. You *(sing. inf.)* are a doctor.

→ .... médico.

c. She is tall.

→ .... alta.

d. They are nice.

→ .... simpáticos.

e. You *(pl. inf.)* are tired.

→ .... cansados.

f. You *(pl. inf.)* are indignant.

→ ....

indignadas.

g. We are content.

→ .... contentas.

h. They are believers.

→ .... creyentes.

i. You *(sing. inf.)* are ill.

→ .... enfermo.

Adjectives with *ser* and *estar*

- Most adjectives require the exclusive use of one or the other (**ser** or **estar**) because their meaning refers either to an essential quality or a temporary state or situation:

  Es inteligente. *He is intelligent.* (essential quality)
  Está solo. *He is alone.* (temporary situation)

- However, some adjectives can be used with either **ser** or **estar** depending on the context. In such cases the meaning changes in line with the usage of **ser** or **estar**:

  Es malo. *He is bad.* (a bad person) / **Está malo.** *He is ill.* (temporary condition)
  El cielo es azul. *The sky is blue.* (general description) / **El cielo está azul.** *The sky is blue.* (it looks blue today)

2 Complete these sentences using the correct form of *ser* or *estar*.

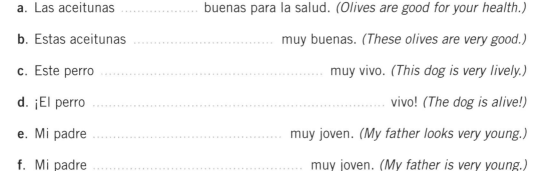

a. Las aceitunas .... buenas para la salud. *(Olives are good for your health.)*

b. Estas aceitunas .... muy buenas. *(These olives are very good.)*

c. Este perro .... muy vivo. *(This dog is very lively.)*

d. ¡El perro .... vivo! *(The dog is alive!)*

e. Mi padre .... muy joven. *(My father looks very young.)*

f. Mi padre .... muy joven. *(My father is very young.)*

g. Mis hermanas .... morenas.
  (My sisters are brunettes.)

h. Mis hermanas .... morenas.
  (My sisters are tanned.)

i. ¡Qué guapa ....!
  (How beautiful you look!)

j. ¡Qué guapa ....!
  (How beautiful you are!)

Ser and estar: expressing location and time

- When *to be* means 'to be located/found', **estar** is used because it describes the condition of something in space at a given time. This is true of both physical location and abstract location (such as an issue or problem, etc.):

  Estoy en París. *I am in Paris.*
  Aquí está la dificultad. *Here is* ('is found') *the difficulty.*

- To talk about specific times (e.g. the hour, day, season, etc.), **ser** is used because these are characteristics that are not dependent on circumstances.

  Hoy es lunes. *Today is Monday.*
  Son las dos de la tarde. *It's two o'clock in the afternoon.*
  En Argentina, **Navidad es en verano.** *In Argentina, Christmas is in the summer.*

- However, if you adopt the point of view of a person experiencing time passing, **estar** can be used, followed by a preposition and the time:

  Estamos a viernes. *It's Friday today.*
  Estáis en invierno. *It's winter where you are now.*

3 Use the context to help you complete these sentences using the correct form of *ser* or *estar*.

a. La solución no .... evidente.

b. Nosotros .... en París.

c. El problema no .... ahí.

d. ¿Qué día .... hoy?

e. Yo .... inglés, ... de Londres.

f. .... la una de la tarde.

g. La fiesta nacional .... el 12 de octubre.

h. ¿Qué hora ....?

i. La solución .... en el trabajo.

j. Mi cumpleaños .... en primavera.

k. No te veo: ¿dónde ....?

l. Perdón, ¿a qué día .... hoy?

m. El problema .... importante.

n. El interés de la película .... en los personajes.

o. Pedro no .... en casa.

p. .... la una de la mañana.

q. Nochebuena.................... la noche del 24 de diciembre.

The present participle and the progressive tenses

- The present participle is the verb form ending in *-ing* in English, e.g. *singing*. In Spanish it is formed by replacing the infinitive ending with the following endings:

  -ar verbs ➜ **-ando**: **cantar** ➜ **cantando**
  -er and **-ir** verbs ➜ **-iendo**: **aprender** ➜ **aprendiendo** / **escribir** ➜ **escribiendo**

- The present participle is most frequently used in progressive tenses (i.e. a conjugated form of **estar** + present participle), also known as continuous tenses. These are used to express an action that is currently in progress:

  Estoy trabajando. *I am working.*

- Occasionally, the present participle is used in constructions such as the following, but this is rarer:

  Viajando se aprende mucho. *By travelling you learn a lot.*

4 Rewrite these sentences in the present progressive. ●●

a. Abro la puerta. ➜ ....

b. ¿A quién llamáis? ➜ ....

c. Compramos el pan. ➜ ....

5 Find six present participles in this grid (vertical, horizontal, diagonal, forwards or backwards), list them and then give their infinitive form. ●●

B	A	I	L	A	N	D	O	O
U	C	F	Y	B	O	I	D	D
T	U	O	H	E	U	N	N	N
R	N	U	M	B	E	D	A	A
E	D	L	A	I	T	O	C	L
D	I	L	V	E	E	N	O	B
O	T	I	O	N	A	N	T	A
N	V	T	U	D	H	A	D	H
A	E	C	N	O	C	U	R	O

Present participle	Infinitive
....	....
....	....
....	....
....	....
....	....
....	....

6 Use the verbs that you found in the previous exercise to complete these sentences in the present progressive tense.

a. Pedro y Juan .... una buena paella.

b. Yo .... vino y tú .... cerveza.

c. Mi hermano .... la guitarra con sus amigos.

d. Este año nosotros .... en Londres.

e. Lo que vosotros .... no es reggaetón, es cumbia.

f. ¿De qué me ....? ¡No te entiendo!

Other uses of *ser* and *estar*

- 'It's me, it's you', etc. are formed with **ser**, followed by the subject pronoun.

  Soy yo. *It's me.*
  Eres tú. *It's you.*
  Es él. *It's him.*

- 'Is … there? / Are … there?' are formed with **estar**, conjugated accordingly.

  ¿Estás? *Are you there?*
  ¿Está Pedro? *Is Pedro there?*

- With the preposition **de**: **ser** indicates (a) what something is made of, (b) origin, or (c) possession; **estar** indicates a temporary situation in time or space or a state of mind.

  Es de plástico. *It's made of plastic.*   **Estoy de vacaciones.** *I'm on holiday.*
  Es de Madrid. *He's from Madrid.*   **Estoy de pie.** *I'm standing up.*
  Es de Pedro. *It's Pedro's.*   **Estoy de mal humor.** *I'm in a bad mood.*

7 Complete these exchanges with the correct conjugated form of 'to be'.

a. – ¿Quién es el siguiente?

  – ¡................. yo!

b. – ¿Quiénes son los padres de este niño?

  – ¡................. nosotros!

c. – ¿Quiénes son los primeros?

  – ¡................. ellos!

d. – ¿Quién es el amo de este perro?

  – ¡................. usted!

8 Complete these sentences with the appropriate form of *ser* or *estar.*

a. Este anillo no .... de oro.

b. ¿De quién .... este anillo?

c. Tú .... de buen humor.

d. ¿Usted .... de Madrid?

e. ¿Usted .... de aquí?

f. No, nosotros no .... de aquí.

g. Nosotros .... de viaje por España.

h. Yo .... de fiesta con unos amigos.

9 *Ser* or *estar*? Choose the correct verbs in this telephone conversation.

Hola, ¿**está** / **estás** Carmen?

Sí, **soy** / **estoy** yo.

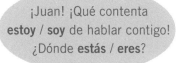

¡Carmen! **Soy** / **Estoy** Juan, ¿cómo **estás** / **eres**?

¡Juan! ¡Qué contenta **estoy** / **soy** de hablar contigo! ¿Dónde **estás** / **eres**?

Estamos / **somos** de fin de semana en Londres Isabel y yo.

Well done! You've completed Lesson 5. Now count up the icons for each exercise and record your result here and in the table on page 128.

6

Present tense irregularities & simple sentences

Stem-changing verbs

- Certain verbs undergo a spelling change in the stem vowel in the present tense:
  - the **-o** becomes **-ue** (d<u>o</u>rmir → d<u>ue</u>rmo, d<u>ue</u>rmes *I sleep, you sleep*, etc.)
  - the **-e** becomes **-ie** (ent<u>e</u>nder → ent<u>ie</u>ndo, ent<u>ie</u>ndes *I understand*, etc.)

- These changes occur only in certain persons. The first- and second-person plural do not have this spelling change (see the verb conjugation tables, pp. 114–117).

- Stem-changing verbs occur in all three verb groups:
  - ending in **-ar**: **contar** *to tell, to count*, **cerrar** *to close*, **sentarse** *to sit down*, **pensar en** *to think (about)*, **acordarse de** *to remember*
  - ending in **-er**: **entender** *to understand*, **volver** *to return*, **poder** *to be able, can*, **perder** *to lose*
  - ending in **-ir**: **divertirse** *to have fun, to enjoy oneself*, **mentir** *to (tell a) lie*

1 Complete the sentences with the appropriate form of these stem-changing verbs.

acordarse · cerrar · contar · entender · dormir · sentarse · mentir · pensar · poder · volver · divertirse · perder

a. Los niños .... frecuentemente a sus padres.

b. Yo .... mucho con la consola.

c. Cuando .... del trabajo, estoy muy cansado.

d. Cuando estamos lejos, no .... de las personas.

e. ¿Tú .... lo que te estoy explicando?

f. Te quiero mucho y .... mucho en ti.

g. ¿Vosotros .... la puerta con llave cuando salís?

h. La clase comienza cuando los alumnos ....

i. Los abuelos siempre .... historias a sus nietos.

j. Nosotros .... mucho tiempo jugando con la Play.

k. Mi hijo de dos años es muy listo: ¡ .... hasta diez!

l. ¿Vosotros .... la siesta por las tardes?

The verb endings -go and -zco

- Ten very common verbs have the irregular ending **-go** in the first-person singular present tense. The other persons in the present tense do not have this change.

  - **caer** *to fall* ➜ **caigo, caes**, etc.
  - **hacer** *to do, to make* ➜ **hago, haces**, etc.
  - **poner** *to put* ➜ **pongo, pones**, etc.
  - **tener** *to have* ➜ **tengo, tienes**, etc.
  - **valer** *to be worth* ➜ **valgo, vales**, etc.
  - **decir** *to say, to tell* ➜ **digo, dices**, etc.
  - **oír** *to hear* ➜ **oigo, oyes**, etc.
  - **salir** *to leave* ➜ **salgo, sales**, etc.
  - **traer** *to bring* ➜ **traigo, traes**, etc.
  - **venir** *to come* ➜ **vengo, vienes**, etc.

- Almost all verbs whose infinitive ends in **-cer** or **-cir** (one exception is **hacer**, see above) have the irregular ending **-zco** in the first-person singular present tense. The other persons in the present tense do not have this change.

  - **conocer** *to know* ➜ **conozco, conoces**, etc.
  - **nacer** *to be born* ➜ **nazco, naces**, etc.
  - **parecer** *to seem* ➜ **parezco, pareces**, etc.
  - **conducir** *to drive* ➜ **conduzco, conduces**, etc.

2 Answer these questions in the negative in the first-person singular.

a. ¿Conoces Barcelona?

→ No, no ....

b. ¿Oyes algo?

→ No, no ....

c. ¿Sales a pasear?

→ ....

d. ¿Te pones la gabardina?

→ ....

e. ¿Conduces bien?

→ ....

f. ¿Haces algo?

→ ....

g. ¿Dices algo?

→ ....

h. ¿Tienes dinero?

→ ....

i. ¿Vienes conmigo?

→ ....

j. ¿Traduces del inglés?

→ ....

k. ¿Me reconoces?

→ ....

l. ¿Me obedeces?

→ ....

Forming questions

- In English, the auxiliary verb *to do* is used with most verbs to ask a question (as well as to form the negative). In Spanish, this is not necessary – the main verb is used on its own. A statement is turned into a question simply by changing the intonation or punctuation:

  ¿Hablas español? *Do you speak Spanish?*
  ¿No hablas español? *Don't you speak Spanish?*

- As in English, there are often various possibilities for word order.

  ¿Es tu hermano el que está hablando? / ¿El que está hablando es tu hermano? / El que está hablando, ¿es tu hermano? *Is your brother the one who is speaking?*

- Some question words are pronouns or adjectives (which change form to agree with the number and gender of the noun), while others are adverbs (which don't change). Question words always have a written accent on the stressed syllable.

  ¿Cómo? *How?*
  ¿Por qué? *Why?*
  ¿Qué? *What?*
  ¿Cuánto? / ¿Cuánta? *How much?* (m./f.)
  ¿Cuántos/-as? *How many?* (m./f.)

  ¿Dónde? *Where?*
  ¿Cuándo? *When?*
  ¿Cuál/Cuáles? *Which?* (sing./pl.)
  ¿Quién/Quiénes? *Who?* (sing./pl.)

3 Write the matching question for each response.

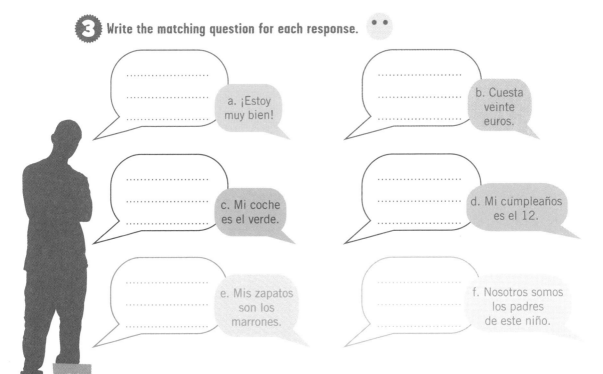

a. ¡Estoy muy bien!

b. Cuesta veinte euros.

c. Mi coche es el verde.

d. Mi cúmpleaños es el 12.

e. Mis zapatos son los marrones.

f. Nosotros somos los padres de este niño.

Forming exclamations

- As with question words, exclamatory words have a written accent.
  - **¡Qué…!** + adjective or noun is used to describe a quality: **¡Qué tonto!** *How silly!* **¡Qué coche!** *What a car!* (Note that with a noun, there is no indefinite article.)
  - **¡Cuánto…!** + verb or **¡Cuánto/-a/-os/-as…!** + noun is used to describe quantity: **¡Cuánto come!** *How he can eat!* **¡Cuántos libros!** *What a lot of books!*

- If an exclamation includes both a noun and an adjective to describe it, the construction is: **¡Qué…!** + noun + **más** (or **tan**) + adjective:

  ¡Qué cosa más rara! *What a strange thing! / How strange!*
  ¡Qué película tan bonita! *What a beautiful film!*

- If an exclamation consists of an entire sentence, the word order must be exclamatory phrase + verb + subject:

  ¡Qué caro es este coche! *How expensive this car is!*
  ¡Cuánto trabajo tienen los alumnos! *What a lot of work the students have!*
  ¡Qué casa más bonita tiene Juan! *What a pretty house Juan has!*

4 Complete these exclamations with the correct word, making it agree if necessary.

a. ¡.............................. habla mi suegra!

b. ¡.......... difíciles son estos problemas!

c. ¡.............. amigas tienes en facebook!

d. ¡......................... alta es esta chica!

e. ¡......................... duermen los bebés!

f. ¡.................. perros hay en esta casa!

g. ¡................................. tarde venís!

h. ¡.............. dinero tiene este hombre!

5 Turn these statements into exclamations.

E.g. A very interesting book → What an interesting book!

a. Un libro muy interesante

→ ....

b. Una perra muy simpática

→ ....

c. Unas playas muy bonitas

→ ....

d. Unos coches muy rápidos

→ ....

6 Turn these statements into exclamations.

E.g. This child seems very tired. → How tired this child seems!

a. Este niño parece muy cansado.

→ ....

b. Estoy muy cansado.

→ ....

c. Tienes un aspecto muy cansado.

→ ....

d. Miguel tiene un perro muy listo.

→ ....

e. Mis amigos cuentan cosas muy divertidas.

→ ....

f. Usted escribe libros muy interesantes.

→ ....

g. Los españoles comen muy tarde.

→ ....

Z Z
Z Z
Z Z
Z

Making comparisons

- *More than / less than* is expressed as **más** + adjective + **que** *more than* / **menos** + adjective + **que** *less than / fewer than*. (Note that this sometimes translates to English comparative *-er* adjectives.)
  Eres más inteligente que yo. *You are more intelligent / smarter than I am.*
  Eres más alto que yo. *You are taller than I am.*
  España es menos poblada que Inglaterra. *Spain is less populated than England.*

- *As … as* can be expressed in two ways:
  - **tan** + adjective + **como**: **Estoy tan cansado como tú.** *I am as tired as you.*
  - **tanto/-a/-os/-as** + noun + **como**: **Tengo tantas hermanas como hermanos.**
    I have as many sisters as brothers.

- There are four adjectives with irregular comparatives: **bueno**, **malo**, **grande** and **pequeño**. The comparatives of the latter two are used to describe age as well as size.
  bueno *good* → **mejor** *better*   **malo** *bad* → **peor** *worse*
  grande *big* → **mayor** *bigger, older*   **pequeño** *small* → **menor** *smaller, younger*

7 Complete these sentences with the correct irregular comparatives.

a. José tiene cuarenta y cinco años, Pedro cincuenta y Juan treinta y ocho: José es .... que Juan y .... que Pedro.

b. Vivir en una ciudad es .... para las diversiones pero el aire es de .... calidad que en el campo.

8 Translate these sentences into Spanish.

a. I've been to ('know') fewer towns than you *(sing. inf.)*.

→ ....

b. I have more books than he does.

→ ....

c. Beer is as expensive as in England.

→ ....

d. I work as many hours as you *(sing. inf.)*.

→ ....

e. He works as much as I do.

→ ....

f. They are as tall as they are stupid.

→ ....

Super! You've completed Lesson 6. It's time to count up the icons for the exercises and record your result here and in the table on page 128.

Vocabulary and comprehension 1: identity & famil

Giving your name, address, profession, etc.

- If you are asked **¿Cuál es tu/su nombre?**, this means your *first name*. The *family name* or *surname* is **el apellido** – or **los apellidos** in the plural, because Spaniards traditionally have two surnames, their father's (**el primer apellido**) and their mother's maiden name (**el segundo apellido**).

- Spaniards must carry an identity card, or **DNI** (**Documento Nacional de Identidad**), on which the parents' first names are also included after '**Hijo/-a de**'. Gender is denoted by **M** (**mujer**) or **V** (**varón**).

- Some common abbreviations for streets and roads: **la calle** *street* is often written as **C/**, **la avenida** *avenue* becomes **Avda.**, and **la plaza** *square* becomes **Pza**. When writing or giving an address, the house number comes after the street name: **C/ San Miguel, 19**, or just **San Miguel, 19**.

- **¿En qué trabajas?** or **¿A qué te dedicas?** *What do you do?* are the two most common ways of asking about someone's job.

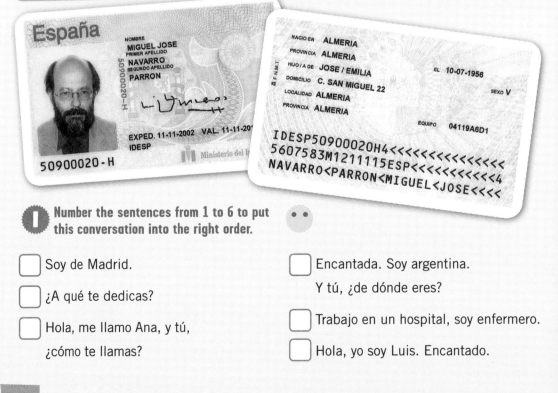

I Number the sentences from 1 to 6 to put this conversation into the right order.

☐ Soy de Madrid.

☐ ¿A qué te dedicas?

☐ Hola, me llamo Ana, y tú, ¿cómo te llamas?

☐ Encantada. Soy argentina. Y tú, ¿de dónde eres?

☐ Trabajo en un hospital, soy enfermero.

☐ Hola, yo soy Luis. Encantado.

2 Use these business cards to connect each question to its answer.

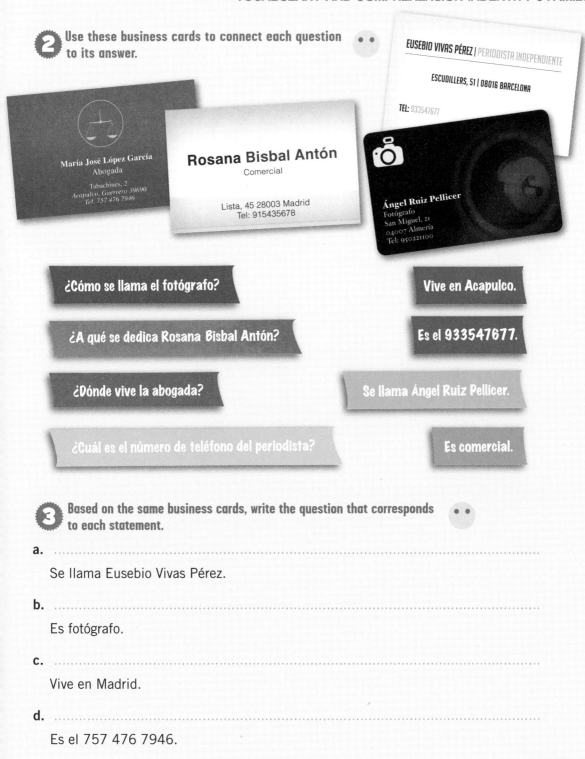

EUSEBIO VIVAS PÉREZ | PERIODISTA INDEPENDIENTE

ESCUDILLERS, 51 | 08016 BARCELONA

TEL: 933547677

María José López García
Abogada
Tabachines, 2
Acapulco, Guerrero 39690
Tel: 757 476 7946

Rosana Bisbal Antón
Comercial

Lista, 45 28003 Madrid
Tel: 915435678

Ángel Ruiz Pellicer
Fotógrafo
San Miguel, 21
04007 Almería
Tel: 950221100

¿Cómo se llama el fotógrafo?

Vive en Acapulco.

¿A qué se dedica Rosana Bisbal Antón?

Es el 933547677.

¿Dónde vive la abogada?

Se llama Ángel Ruiz Pellicer.

¿Cuál es el número de teléfono del periodista?

Es comercial.

3 Based on the same business cards, write the question that corresponds to each statement.

a. ....

Se llama Eusebio Vivas Pérez.

b. ....

Es fotógrafo.

c. ....

Vive en Madrid.

d. ....

Es el 757 476 7946.

Family names in Spain

- Not all Spaniards are called **Martínez** or **González**, although the **-ez** ending is indeed very common. In fact, it is an archaic suffix meaning 'son of': 'son of Martín', 'son of Gonzalo', etc. To find out the most common surname of all, read this news article.

Useful words:

- **cada** *each*
- **mismo** *same*
- **usuario** *user*
- **todo** *all*

- **otro(s) tanto(s), otra(s) tanta(s)** *just as many*
- **tras** *after*

Un país de Marías y Garcías

Seis millones de mujeres se llaman María y tres millones de hombres José

María para ellas. José para ellos. Son los nombres que más abundan en la población de España. Incluyendo los nombres compuestos (María del Carmen, María del Mar…), lo llevan 274 de cada mil mujeres. Entre los 22,5 millones de hombres, ocurre lo mismo con José, con tres millones de usuarios (130 de cada mil españoles). Y de apellido, sobre todo García: lo lleva en primer lugar en torno a un millón y medio de personas. Para otras tantas es el segundo. O sea, que consta en el DNI de siete de cada 100 residentes en España. Y tras García, González, Fernández y Rodríguez (cada uno de ellos lo llevan de primero casi 900.000 personas).

4 Find the equivalent of phrases a and b in the text, then translate phrases c and d.

a. 274 women out of 1000 → ....

b. 7 residents out of 100 → ....

c. One man in ten → ....

d. Three out of four women → ....

5 For each sentence below, tick true or false according to the information in the article.

VERDADERO FALSO

a. Unas 900.000 personas se apellidan Rodríguez de primer apellido. →

b. Unas 900.000 personas se apellidan García Rodríguez. →

c. 1.500.000 personas se llaman García de primer apellido. →

d. 1.500.000 personas se llaman García de segundo apellido. →

e. 3.000.000 personas se llaman García de primer apellido. →

f. 3.000.000 personas se llaman García de segundo apellido. →

First names

Traditionally, many people were named after saints in Spain and would celebrate their saint's feast day or name day (**la onomástica**) as much as their birthday (**el cumpleaños**).

Nicknames are common in Spain: **Pedrito** for **Pedro**, **Isabelita** for **Isabel**, etc. Some do not sound much like the proper name! For example, **Pepe** for **José**, **Paco** for **Francisco**, **Lola** for **Dolores**, etc.

Useful words:

- **siglo** *century*

- **hasta** *until*

- **seguir, seguido** *to follow, followed*

LOS NOMBRES: UN SIGLO DE MODAS

Entre comienzos del siglo XX y finales de los años treinta, los nombres más frecuentes para las mujeres son María (campeón absoluto) y Carmen. Con los hombres, José es el nombre más habitual hasta los cuarenta. En los años cincuenta y sesenta Antonio fue el preferido, combinado con José. En los setenta, David se convierte en líder absoluto hasta comienzos del siglo XXI. A partir de 2000, Alejandro es el bautismo más frecuente, seguido por Daniel, Pablo o Adrián.

6 Fill in the following table using the information in the article:
- add an 'x' if the name is the most popular in that decade.
- add a double 'xx' if the name is the second (or third or fourth) most popular.
- leave the box empty if there is no information for that decade.

	1900 1910	1910 1920	1930 1940	1940 1950	1950 1960	1960 1970	1970 1980	1980 1990	1990 2000	2000 ....
Adrián										
Alejandro										
José Antonio										
Daniel										
David										
José										
Pablo										

7 Find the equivalent of phrases a, b, c in the article, then translate phrases d, e, f.

a. The 21ˢᵗ century → ....

b. The beginning of the 20ᵗʰ century → ....

c. The end of the 1930s → ....

d. Until the end of the 1950s → ....

e. From the beginning of the 1980s → ....

f. The 20ᵗʰ century → ....

Family and in-laws

The word **la familia** refers to one's *immediate family*. The extended family is **la familia política** *in-laws, family related by marriage*. As regards step-families, although you'll find the words **padrastro** *stepfather*, **madrastra** *stepmother*, **hermanastro/-a** *half-brother / half-sister* in the dictionary, today these are rarely used as they have a negative connotation. Instead people tend to say **el marido de mi madre**, **la mujer de mi padre** or simply **mi hermano/-a**, without explaining further.

Useful words:

- **padre, madre** *father, mother*
- **hermano, hermana** *brother, sister*
- **tío, tía** *uncle, aunt*
- **sobrino, sobrina** *nephew, niece*
- **primo, prima** *cousin* (m./f.)
- **abuelo, abuela** *grandfather, grandmother*
- **nieto, nieta** *grandson, granddaughter*

- **cuñado** *brother-in-law*
- **cuñada** *sister-in-law*
- **yerno** *son-in-law*
- **nuera** *daughter-in-law*
- **suegro** *father-in-law*
- **suegra** *mother-in-law*

8 Try to remember the words for the different relatives without looking back at the previous page and complete this family tree using the information provided. Place the correct name under each picture.

a. Paula no tiene hermanos.

b. Javier es el yerno de Carmen.

c. Antonio es el tío de Paula.

d. Andrés es el sobrino de Antonio.

e. Juan es el nieto de José.

f. Lucía es la hermana mayor ('older') de Dolores.

g. Dolores y Luisa son primas.

h. Rocío es la cuñada de Lorenzo.

i. María es la madre de Lucía.

Great work! You've completed the first Vocabulary and Comprehension section. Count up the icons for the exercises and record your result here and in the table on page 128.

43

7

Verb phrases & more present tense irregularities

Expressing a repeated action

- Spanish has a number of verb phrases in which a helping verb is used to modify the meaning of another verb, particularly to express concepts such as the repetition, frequency or continuation of an action. For example, to convey a repeated action, the verb phrase **volver a** + infinitive is used (**volver** is conjugated – careful, it is a stem-changing verb):

  Vuelvo a abrir el libro. *I reopen the book. / I open the book again.*
  Volvemos a cantar. *We are singing again.*

- The same idea can be expressed using the adverbial phases **de nuevo** or **otra vez**.

  Canto de nuevo. *I'm singing again.*
  Abro el libro otra vez. *I open the book once more.*

1 Convey the idea of repetition in these sentences, replacing the adverbial phrase with a verb phrase. Retain the same grammatical person.

a. Llama de nuevo a su hijo.

➜ ....

b. Contáis otra vez la misma historia.

➜ ....

c. El niño miente otra vez.

➜ ....

d. Nazco de nuevo.

➜ ....

e. Cierran de nuevo la puerta.

➜ ....

f. Estamos juntos otra vez.

➜ ....

g. Trabajan de nuevo en Madrid.

➜ ....

h. Usted viaja a España otra vez.

➜ ....

i. Somos amigos de nuevo.

➜ ....

j. Leemos otra vez este libro.

➜ ....

Expressing a habitual action

- To talk about something one does often, the verb phrase is **soler** + infinitive (**soler** is conjugated – it is a stem-changing verb). Another option is to use the adverbial phrases **a menudo** *often,* **con frecuencia** *frequently* or **habitualmente** *regularly.*

  Suelo ir (or **Voy a menudo**) **a la piscina.** *I often go to the swimming pool.*
  Suelen cenar (or **Cenan habitualmente**) **a las diez.** *They usually dine at ten.*

2 Convey the idea of habitual action in these sentences, replacing the adverbial phrase with a verb phrase. Retain the same grammatical person.

a. Mi abuelo se acuerda a menudo de mí.

→ ....

b. Conduzco a menudo una moto.

→ ....

c. Pierdes tus llaves con frecuencia.

→ ....

d. Me siento a menudo en este banco.

→ ....

e. Hacemos deporte con frecuencia.

→ ....

f. Habitualmente usted entiende rápido.

→ ....

g. Habláis a menudo inglés.

→ ....

h. Comes habitualmente a las tres.

→ ....

i. ¿Sales con frecuencia a bailar?

→ ....

j. Estamos a menudo en casa.

→ ....

45

Stem-changing verbs

- In certain **-ir** verbs, the **e** in the verb stem changes to an **i** when conjugated in certain persons. In the present tense, this occurs in every person except the first- and second-person plural. For example, **pedir** *to ask for*: **pido, pides, pide, pedimos, pedís, piden**.

- Some other verbs that have the same stem change are: **medir** *to measure*, **seguir** *to follow*, **despedirse** *to say goodbye, to take leave*, **reír** *to laugh*, **sonreír** *to smile*, **repetir** *to repeat*, **vestir** *to dress, to wear*, **servir** *to serve*.

- Note that if there is more than one **e** in the verb stem, this change only affects the final **e**: **despedirse** *to say goodbye* → **me despido** *I say goodbye*, **repetir** *to repeat* → **repito** *I repeat*, etc.

3 Cross out the six incorrect forms of the present tense conjugation of *reír*, then write the correct conjugation in the right order below.

Present tense of *reír*

....

....

....

....

....

ríes	reímos	rein
reís	riemos	río
rien	reo	rei
riéis	ríe	rees

4 Here are seven e → i stem-changing verbs. Put them into the appropriate following sentences using the correct conjugated form.

medir vestir servir despedirse pedir sonreír repetir

a. ¿Por qué ....? ¿Pensáis en algo divertido?

b. Tú, ¿cómo .... de la gente: das un beso o das la mano?

c. Mi hermano .... un metro noventa.

d. Nosotros siempre .... pantalones vaqueros.

e. Los niños siempre .... dinero a los padres.

f. Camarero, ¿me .... usted una cerveza, por favor?

g. Si no .... muchas veces la conjugación, no me acuerdo.

5 Translate these phrases into Spanish.

a. I serve: ....

b. We repeat: ....

c. You *(sing. inf.)* ask for: ....

d. He says goodbye: ....

e. They measure: ....

f. You *(sing. for.)* laugh, sir:

....

g. You *(pl.)* smile, my friends:

....

h. I wear: ....

More irregularities

- As we've seen, **decir** is irregular in the first-person present tense, becoming **digo** with a **g**. But note that it also has the **e ➔ i** stem change: **d<u>e</u>cir ➔ digo, d<u>i</u>ces, d<u>i</u>ce, decimos, decís, d<u>i</u>cen**.

- Two more verbs with the **e ➔ i** stem change are **s<u>e</u>guir** *to follow* and **elegir** *to choose*. But note that these verbs (like all those with a stem ending in **-g** or **-gu**) also take a spelling change with conjugation endings starting with **-a** or **-o** in order to retain the same pronunciation:

  - before **a** or **o** the **-g** becomes **-j**: **elijo** *I choose* (to retain the guttural **g** sound)
  - before **a** or **o** the **-gu** becomes **-g**: **sigo** *I follow* (to retain the hard **g** sound)

- Finally, note that the present participle of **e ➔ i** stem-changing verbs also changes:

  p<u>e</u>dir *to ask for* ➔ **p<u>i</u>diendo** *asking for*
  d<u>e</u>cir *to say, tell* ➔ **d<u>i</u>ciendo** *saying, telling*

6 Rewrite these sentences in the present progressive.

a. ¿Qué dices? → ....

b. ¿Por qué sonríe usted? → ....

c. Mis hermanas se visten. → ....

d. No pedimos nada. → ....

e. Repito la lección. → ....

f. No medís bien. → ....

g. Se despide de la abuela. → ....

7 Complete these sentences using the correct conjugated form of *seguir* or *elegir*.

a. Entre París y Londres yo .... París.

b. ¿ .... o abandonáis la carrera?

c. Usted .... muy bien los colores con que viste.

d. Estoy cansado: no ....

e. Entre carne y pescado, nosotros
   .... pescado.

f. Es un perro fiel: siempre ....
   a su amo.

g. Los gatos son independientes:
   no .... a nadie.

h. ....
   a tus amigos pero no a tus familiares.

Expressing a continuing action: *seguir* + present participle

- To convey an action that began in the past and continues into the present (i.e. *to go on/keep doing something*), the verb phrase is **seguir** (conjugated) + present participle.

  Sigo trabajando en el turismo. *I still work in the tourist industry.*
  Seguimos viviendo en Madrid. *We still live in Madrid.*

- Alternatively, the adverbs **aún** and **todavía** can be used, which translate to *still* in this context.

  Vivimos aún en Madrid. *We still live in Madrid.*
  ¿Todavía estás trabajando? *Are you still working?*

8 Rewrite these sentences replacing the adverbs *aún* and *todavía* with the verb phrase that expresses continuation. Retain the grammatical person used in the original sentence.

a. Aún escribo a mano. → ....

b. Todavía existen personas sin ordenador. → ....

c. Mi vieja pluma aún sirve. → ....

d. Y tú, ¿todavía usas pluma y papel? → ....

e. Usted aún hace las cosas como antes. → ....

f. Aún sois fieles al pasado. → ....

g. Todavía sonreímos con las películas de Charlie Chaplin.

→ ....

¡Muy bien! You've reached the end of Lesson 7. It's time to count up the icons for the exercises and record your result here and in the table on page 128.

8

The present subjunctive

The present subjunctive

The subjunctive is a grammatical mood used to express 'unreality': wish, possibility, opinion or intention. (The indicative mood is used to state objective facts.)

- The most frequent use is in subordinate clauses, usually after the word **que** *that* when there is a change in subject:
  Quiero que cantes. *I want you to sing.* ('I want that you sing.')

- It is formed using the stem of the first-person singular present indicative and adding an ending: the ending starts with **-e** for **-ar** verbs, and with **-a** for **-er** or **-ir** verbs.
  cantar: cante, cantes, cante, cantemos, cantéis, canten
  comer: coma, comas, coma, comamos, comáis, coman
  subir: suba, subas, suba, subamos, subáis, suban

- If the first-person present indicative is irregular, this irregularity occurs in all persons:
  decir (digo *I say***) → diga, digas, diga, digamos, digáis, digan**
  conocer (conozco *I know***) → conozca, conozcas, conozca,** etc.
  pedir (pido *I ask for***) → pida, pidas, pida,** etc.

- However, most stem-changing verbs (apart from **e → i** verbs), have no stem change in the first- and second-person plural of the subjunctive (or in the indicative).
  contar: cuente, cuentes, cuente, contemos, contéis, cuenten

1 Complete this table with the missing infinitives and the present subjunctive forms for each person.

infinitive	yo	tú	él, ella, usted	nosotros, nosotras	vosotros, vosotras	ellos, ellas
cantar						
						escriban
	salga					
		vistas				
				pensemos		
			lea			
					conozcáis	

2 Complete the following sentences with the correct verb forms from the previous table.

a. Hola, abuela, este libro es para ti, para que lo .... pensando en mí.

b. Quiero que vosotros le .... una bonita carta a la abuela.

c. A la abuela no le gusta Mario: no quiere que su nieta .... con él.

d. La abuela quiere que nosotros .... bien para su cumpleaños.

e. Queremos que usted también .... a la abuela.

f. La abuela me llama muy a menudo para que siempre .... en ella.

g. La abuela quiere que sus nietos le .... la canción del cumpleaños feliz.

3 Although Santa Claus is gaining ground in Spain, most children write to the Three Kings (*los Reyes Magos*) to ask for presents, which they receive on 6 January. In this letter, underline the four verbs in the present subjunctive.

Queridos Reyes Magos:

Soy un niño bueno y obediente que quiere mucho a sus padres. Por eso quiero que me traigáis un tren eléctrico muy grande, con muchos vagones para que pueda jugar con todos mis amigos.

Ah, si es posible, también quiero que vengáis antes del 6 de enero porque el 8 vuelvo al cole y mis padres no quieren que juegue cuando hay escuela.

¡Muchas gracias!
Manolito.

4 Complete this table with all the present subjunctive forms of the four verbs that you found in Manolito's letter.

infinitive				
yo				
tú				
él, ella, usted				
nosotros/-as				
vosotros/-as				
ellos, ellas, ustedes				

Expressing wishes and regrets

The present subjunctive is also used to express wishes or regrets in independent clauses.

- A common way to express a wish is **ojalá** *hopefully* (from the Arabic ***Insha'Allah*** 'God willing') + subjunctive. Another option is **¡Que…!** + subjunctive, which is equivalent to indirect commands such as 'May he rest in peace.'

  Ojalá pueda venir. *Let's hope that he can come.*
  Ojalá haga buen tiempo. *Let's hope the weather will be good.*
  ¡Que volváis pronto! *[May you] come back soon!*
  ¡Que tengas suerte! *[May you have] good luck!*

- A common way to express regret is **Lástima que…** or **Qué pena que…** *What a pity that…* + subjunctive.

  Lástima que no estés aquí. *Pity that you won't be here.*
  Qué pena que no vengas. *It's a shame you're not coming.*

5 Translate these wishes using *que* + subjunctive.

a. Live *(pl.)* happy! → ....

b. Dance *(pl.)* well! → ....

c. Enjoy yourself *(inf. sing.)*! → ....

d. Come back *(inf. sing.)* soon! → ....

6 Use *ojalá* to form sentences that express wishes based on the words given.

a. ellos / tener un buen viaje

→ ....

b. usted / vivir muchos años

→ ....

c. yo / poder asistir a tu cumpleaños

→ ....

d. vosotros / gustar esta paella

→ ....

e. tú / entender el problema → ....

f. nosotros / volver a España → ....

g. los Reyes Magos / traer muchos regalos → ....

h. tú / seguir teniendo suerte → ....

¡Ojalá ....!

¡Ojalá ....!

¡Ojala ....!

7 Express regrets based on the statements provided. Retain the grammatical person and conjugate the verb in the appropriate form.

a. No hablamos inglés. Qué lástima que no ....

b. No bebéis cerveza. Qué lástima que no ....

c. No me gusta bailar. Qué lástima que no ....

d. No bailas bien. Qué lástima que no ....

e. No conocen a mi hermana. Qué lástima que no ....

f. No oyes bien. Qué lástima que no ....

g. No sirvo para nada. Qué lástima que no ....

h. No sonríen nunca. Qué lástima que no ....

Negative commands ('Don't ...!'): informal and formal

• As we've seen, there are different forms of *you* in Spanish. These are **tú** (informal sing.), **usted** (formal sing.), **vosotros/-as** (informal pl.) and **ustedes** (formal pl.). Each is used with a different verb form, e.g.:

Tú eres mi amigo. / Vosotros sois mis amigos. (second-person sing./pl.)
Usted es mi amigo. / Ustedes son mis amigos. (third-person sing./pl.)

• Because commands (affirmative or negative) address *you*, there are also four possible command forms in Spanish. A negative command (telling someone not to do something) is expressed using **no** + present subjunctive in one of the four persons described above:

¡No cantes! *Don't sing!* (informal) (second-person singular)
¡No cantéis! *Don't sing!* (informal) (second-person plural)
¡No cante (usted)! *Don't sing!* (formal) (third-person singular)
¡No canten (ustedes)! *Don't sing!* (formal) (third-person plural)

8 Tick whether each negative command is formal or informal, then rewrite them using the other form of address.

	Tú	Usted	
a.	☐	☐	....
b.	☐	☐	....
c.	☐	☐	....
d.	☐	☐	....
e.	☐	☐	....
f.	☐	☐	....
g.	☐	☐	....
h.	☐	☐	....

a. ¡No haga eso!

b. ¡No coma paella!

c. ¡No lean ese libro!

d. ¡No cierres la puerta!

e. ¡No os sentéis aquí!

f. ¡No conduzcan tan rápido!

g. ¡No digáis palabrotas!

h. ¡No repitas esa palabra!

Ways of saying 'perhaps'

There are various ways to say *maybe*, *perhaps*:

- **acaso**, **quizás** and **tal vez** are usually followed by the subjunctive (unless what follows is in little doubt, in which case the indicative can be used):

  Acaso no te oiga. *Perhaps she doesn't hear you.*
  Quizás vuelva tarde esta noche. *I may possibly return late tonight.*
  Tal vez no hable español. *Maybe he doesn't speak Spanish.*

- **a lo mejor**, however, is always followed by the indicative:

  A lo mejor no te oye. *Perhaps she doesn't hear you.*

9 Rewrite these sentences replacing *a lo mejor* with *tal vez*.

a. A lo mejor no abren por la tarde. ➜ ....

b. A lo mejor no comprende el español. ➜ ....

c. A lo mejor no escribís nunca cartas. ➜ ....

d. A lo mejor no haces bien tu trabajo. ➜ ....

e. A lo mejor no lo reconocemos. ➜ ....

f. A lo mejor no me despido de ellos. ➜ ....

g. A lo mejor no me entiende usted. ➜ ....

h. A lo mejor no os acordáis de él. ➜ ....

Excellent! You've completed Lesson 8. It's time to count up the icons for the exercises and record your result here and in the table on page 128.

More on irregular conjugations & the subjunctive

9

Some uniquely irregular verbs

We've seen several types of irregularities and stem changes that occur in certain groups of verbs. But there are also some uniquely irregular verbs that have to be learned by heart (see the tables on pp. 118–121). Here are some of the irregular conjugations of a few of these verbs in the present tense (indicative and subjunctive).

- Present indicative:

  - **caber** *to fit (into)*: <u>quepo</u>, **cabes,** etc.
  - **dar** *to give:* <u>doy</u>, **das, da,** etc.
  - **ir** *to go:* <u>voy</u>, <u>vas</u>, <u>va</u>, <u>vamos</u>, <u>vais</u>, <u>van</u>

  - **oír** *to hear:* <u>oigo</u>, <u>oyes</u>, <u>oye</u>, oímos, oís, <u>oyen</u>
  - **saber** *to know:* <u>sé</u>, **sabes, sabe,** etc.
  - **ver** *to see:* <u>veo</u>, **ves, ve,** etc.

- Present subjunctive:

  - **estar:** <u>esté</u>, <u>estés</u>, <u>esté</u>, etc. • **ser:** <u>sea</u>, <u>seas</u>, <u>sea</u>, etc. • **saber:** <u>sepa</u>, <u>sepas</u>, <u>sepa</u>, etc.
  - **ir:** <u>vaya</u>, <u>vayas</u>, <u>vaya</u>, etc.   • **ver:** <u>vea</u>, <u>veas</u>, <u>vea</u>, etc.

I Find 11 conjugated forms of the verbs above in this *sopa de letras*. Then write the infinitive form, starting with the horizontal verbs, followed by the vertical verbs. Lastly, tick the mood of each verb.

Infinitive	Indicative	Subjunctive
a.	⬭	⬭
b.	⬭	⬭
c.	⬭	⬭
d.	⬭	⬭
e.	⬭	⬭
f.	⬭	⬭
g.	⬭	⬭
h.	⬭	⬭
i.	⬭	⬭
j.	⬭	⬭
k.	⬭	⬭

U	V	E	E	I	S	A	E
L	V	A	Y	A	M	O	S
C	A	B	E	N	U	I	T
O	I	T	O	M	S	S	É
I	S	Y	V	U	E	T	I
G	V	S	E	P	Á	I	S
O	E	I	A	R	I	S	O
D	O	Y	N	O	S	T	I

Complete the sentences with the verb forms that you found in the *sopa de letras*.

a. Este coche es muy espacioso: .... hasta seis personas.

b. ¿Por qué .... siempre a Marbella? ¿Os gusta tanto la playa?

c. Quiero que .... en casa estudiando este fin de semana.

d. Tal vez .... a Sevilla estas vacaciones.

e. No .... dónde está esa calle, quizás lo .... vosotros.

f. ¿Por qué no me ayudáis? No .... tan perezosos.

g. Ojalá lo .... mis ojos.

h. Habla más alto, no te .... bien.

i. No te .... , ¿dónde estás?

j. Te .... un libro para tu hermano.

Stem-changing verbs in the present subjunctive: exceptions

- Although most stem-changing verbs have no stem change in the first- and second-person plural of the subjunctive (nor in the indicative), certain **-ir** verbs do have a stem change in these persons – but not the same stem change!

- There are two models: **sentir** (the **-e** changes to **-i**) and **dormir** (the **-o** changes to **-u**). Note that in all other persons, the normal stem change occurs.

- A few common verbs that have this irregularity are: **divertir, mentir, preferir, sugerir** (model: **sentir**, note that only the final vowel in the stem takes the change, e.g. **pref<u>e</u>rir**) and **morir** (model: **dormir**).

SENTIR	DORMIR
sienta	duerma
sientas	duermas
sienta	duerma
s<u>i</u>ntamos	d<u>u</u>rmamos
s<u>i</u>ntáis	d<u>u</u>rmáis
sientan	duerman

3 Put the correct verb forms into the sentences below.

a. Sois auténticos españoles: .... la siesta por la tarde.

b. Cuando su hijo le ...., el padre está furioso.

c. Si hace mal tiempo, tal vez .... quedarnos en casa.

d. Estamos acostumbrados al frío: no lo ....

e. Qué pena que los toros .... durante las corridas.

f. Ojalá .... mucho durante la fiesta.

g. No nos gusta ver películas en casa: .... salir.

h. Siempre estáis de mal humor: no .... con nada.

i. El padre no quiere que su hijo le ....

j. Pone el radiador para que no .... frío.

k. Ojalá .... bien esta noche.

l. Algunas veces son los matadores los que ....

dormís

mueren

sentimos

mueran

durmáis

os divertís

preferimos

mienta

miente

sintamos

os divirtáis

prefiramos

The subjunctive in subordinate clauses

We've seen that after verbs that express a wish (**querer que, desear que**) or conjunctions that express intent (**para que**), the subjunctive is used in the subordinate clause. Two other common uses of the subjunctive are:

• After a main clause in the negative, such as **no creo que..., no pienso que...**:

No creo que venga. *I don't think that he is coming.*
No piensa que sea correcto. *She doesn't think that it is correct.*

• After a main clause that expresses a feeling or an opinion:

Me gusta que vistas bien. *I like [the fact] that you dress well.*
Me parece bien que vayas a Londres. *I think it's good that you're going to London.*

4 These two people do not share the same opinion. What do you think?
For each exchange, place + next to the opinion you agree with, and −
next to the one you disagree with.

La tecnología hace más felices a los hombres. ☐

☐ Los jóvenes de hoy solo piensan en su móvil.

¡Internet aísla completamente a la gente! ☐

¡Muchos chicos y chicas colaboran en ONG's! ☐

Entender de informática te ayuda a conseguir un trabajo. ☐

☐ Vivimos en un mundo que progresa sin cesar.

¡Miles de personas mueren de hambre cada día! ☐

¡Lo más importante es tener una bonita letra! ☐

Hoy la inmensa mayoría de la gente tiene un ordenador. ☐

¡En muchos países el ordenador sigue siendo un lujo! ☐

5 Now take the five opinions with which you disagreed and rewrite
them based on the sentence starters below.

E.g. No creo que la tecnología .... más felices a los hombres.
or No creo que Internet .... completamente a la gente.

a. No creo que ....

b. No pienso que ....

c. No estoy convencido de que ....

d. No estoy seguro de que ....

e. No es verdad que ....

Subordinate clauses

- Not all subordinate clauses after **que** *that* require the subjunctive. If the main clause states a fact or a thought (*to say that / to think that …*), the indicative mood is used.

  Pienso que Ana está cansada. *I think that Ana is tired.*
  Dice que no tiene dinero. *He says that he doesn't have any money.*
  Me pregunto quién es. *I wonder who it is.* (A written accent appears on a question word even in indirect questions.)

- In Spanish, a wish or command is typically conveyed with **que** + subjunctive, with a change of subject in the subordinate clause. In English this is usually avoided by using an infinitive after the main clause.

  Te pido que vengas rápido. *I'm asking you to come quickly.* ('that you come')
  Le dice que compre la leche. *She tells him to buy the milk.* ('that he buy')

- In some cases, either the indicative or subjunctive can be used, which gives a different shade of meaning:

  Te digo que trabajo. *I'm telling you that I'm working.* (indicative: it's a fact)
  Te digo que trabajes. *I'm telling you to work.* (subjunctive: it's a command)

6 Translate the following sentences.

a. I wonder where he lives.

→ ....

b. I don't know why he drinks.

→ ....

c. I think that they have two children.

→ ....

d. It seems to me that you *(sing. inf.)* don't work.

→ ....

e. Do you *(sing. inf.)* think he's ill?

→ ....

7 Translate the following sentences.

a. You *(sing. inf.)* ask me to help you.

→ ....

b. I ask you *(sing. inf.)* to leave.

→ ....

c. He asks us to repeat [it].

→ ....

d. They ask us to open.

→ ....

e. You *(sing. formal)* ask me to sing.

→ ....
....

8 Translate the following sentences into English using 'to tell/say' + infinitive or 'to tell/say that' + subordinate clause.

a. El profesor nos dice que leamos libros en español.

→ ....

b. El profesor nos dice que leemos muy bien.

→ ....

c. El profesor nos dice que vamos a ver una película.

→ ....

d. El profesor nos dice que vayamos a ver películas.

→ ....

9 Conjugate the verb in parentheses in the indicative or the subjunctive, whichever the case requires.

a. La madre le dice a su hijo que .... prudente con la moto. **(ser)**

b. Le pide que no .... muy rápido. **(ir)**

c. El hijo le dice que no ....
(preocuparse)

d. Le dice que él ....
siempre con prudencia. **(conducir)**

e. Le dice a su madre que ....
tranquila. **(dormir)**

f. Le dice que ....
dormir tranquila. **(poder)**

¡Eso es! You've finished Lesson 9. It's time to count up the icons for the exercises and record your results here and in the table on page 128.

Expressing obligation or need & making commands

Expressing obligation and need

- To say something has to be done without specifying who has to do it, the phrase is **hay que** + infinitive *it is necessary to* ... To specify the person who is obligated, you can use the verb phrase **tener que** (conjugated) + infinitive. Another possibility is the verb **deber** *to have to, must* + infinitive, which implies a moral obligation.
Hay que trabajar. *It is necessary to work.* **Tienes que trabajar.** *You have to work.*
Debo ayudar a mi hermanito. *I have to help my little brother.*

- **Hace falta que** + subjunctive is another way to express obligation, whereas **hace(n) falta** + noun expresses a need (the verb conjugates according to what is needed, i.e. in the third-person singular or plural).
Hace falta que trabajes mucho. *You must work hard.*
Hace falta dinero para vivir. *One needs money to live.*

- Or *to need* can be translated literally using **necesitar** followed by a direct object:
Necesito tu ayuda. *I need your help.*

I Translate these sentences that express a need into Spanish.

a. He needs a computer. ➜ ....

b. Do you *(sing. inf.)* need me? ➜ ....

c. I don't need you *(sing. inf.)*. ➜ ....

d. Do you need money, sir? ➜ ....

e. We need Carmen. ➜ ....

f. A computer is necessary in order to work. ➜ ....

g. Are sunglasses needed? ➜ ....

h. There have to be prawns in paella. ➜ ....

i. To make a Spanish omelette, eggs are necessary. ➜ ....

j. Do we need bread? ➜ ....

2 Complete these sentences using *hay que* or *hace falta que* and then translate them.

a. ¿.............................. sentarse aquí?

→ ....

b. ¿.............................. compremos pan?

→ ....

c. ¿.............................. venga Pedro?

→ ....

d. No .... mentir.

→ ....

e. .... cerrar la puerta.

→ ....

f. .... vuelvas.

→ ....

g. .... viajar a menudo.

→ ....

h. .... leer libros.

→ ....

i. .... lo sepas.

→ ....

3 Express these obligations using *hace falta que*, retaining the same grammatical person.

a. Tienen que hablar con él.

→ ....

b. Tenemos que leer este libro.

→ ....

c. Tenéis que ser pacientes.

→ ....

d. Tienes que seguir estudiando.

→ ....

4 Express these obligations using *tener que*, retaining the same grammatical person.

a. Hace falta que hagas un esfuerzo.

→ ....

b. No hace falta que pidáis ayuda.

→ ....

c. ¿Hace falta que vaya yo?

→ ....

d. Hace falta que estemos tranquilos.

→ ....

Commands (the imperative)

Commands are used when telling someone to do something. They use what is called the imperative form of the verb. Here are the <u>informal</u> imperative forms in Spanish.

- To address one person informally, the imperative is the same as the second-person singular present indicative, but without the **-s**:

¡Canta! *Sing!* **¡Come!** *Eat!*
¡Piensa! *Think!* **¡Repite!** *Repeat!*

- To address more than one person informally, just replace the **-r** ending of the infinitive with **-d**:

¡Cantad! *Sing!* **¡Comed!** *Eat!*
¡Pensad! *Think!* **¡Repetid!** *Repeat!*

- In the singular, there are 8 irregular imperatives (see box).

> **8 IRREGULAR IMPERATIVES**
>
> **¡Haz!** *Do!/Make!*
> **¡Pon!** *Put!/Place!*
> **¡Ten!** *Have!*
> **¡Sal!** *Leave!*
> **¡Ven!** *Come!*
> **¡Di!** *Say!*
> **!Sé!** *Be!*
> **¡Ve!** *Go!*

5 Complete this table with the correct informal imperative forms.

INFINITIVE	hablar					cerrar
tú		di		pide		
vosotros/-as			haced		id	

6 Use the imperative forms from the table above to complete the following informal commands. Pay attention to whether one person *(tú)* or more than one person *(vosotros/-as)* is/are being addressed.

a. No os oigo: ¡ .... un poco más alto, por favor!

b. ¡ .... la verdad! ¿Me quieres o no?

c. ¡Niños, antes de jugar, ... los deberes para la escuela!

d. Isabel, ¡.. a comprar el pan, por favor!

e. ¡ .... bien la puerta! Os lo pido por favor.

f. Hoy es tu cumpleaños: .... lo que quieres comer.

Using pronouns with commands

- If an object pronoun is used with an affirmative imperative (i.e. telling someone to do something), it is attached to the end of the verb, forming a single word. The stress stays on the same syllable of the verb, so usually a written accent is needed:

  ¡Háblame! *Speak to me!*   **¡Léelo!** *Read it!*

- If two pronouns are attached to the imperative, the indirect object (usually referring to a person) always comes before the direct object (see Lesson 3, page 15). The stress still says on the same syllable of the verb:

  ¡Dímelo! *Say it to me!*   **¡Cuéntanoslo!** *Tell it to us!*
  ¡Léeselo! *Read it to him!*

- Reflexive verbs by their very nature are always followed by an object pronoun: **lavarse → ¡Lávate las manos!** *Wash your hands!* (sing. inf.) **¡Siéntate!** *Sit down!* (sing. inf.). In the plural (**vosotros/-as**) imperative of reflexive verbs, the final **-d** is dropped before the pronoun **os**.

  ¡Lavaos las manos! *Wash your hands!* (pl.)
  ¡Sentaos! *Sit down!* (pl.)

 7 Rewrite these sentences, replacing *tener que* + infinitive with the correct imperative form and replacing the words in italics with indirect and/or direct object pronouns. Don't forget the written accent on the verb!

E.g. (sentence a): The Spanish equivalent of 'Tell it to him'.

a. Tenéis que contar *esa historia a Pedro.* → ....

b. Tienes que llamar *a tu hermano.* → ....

c. *Te* tienes que poner *la gabardina.* → ....

d. Tenéis que escribir *diez correos.* → ....

e. Tenéis que probar *estas cervezas.* → ....

f. Tienes que dar *ese regalo a la abuela.* → ....

g. Tienes que entender *a Isabel.* → ....

h. Tenéis que conducir *este coche.* → ....

8 Rephrase the obligation, replacing *tener que* + infinitive with the correct imperative form in each sentence.

a. Tienes que acordarte de mí. ....

b. Tenéis que acordaros de él. ....

c. Tenéis que divertiros mucho. ....

d. Tienes que divertirte en esa fiesta. ....

Formal commands

We've seen the informal imperative in both the singular (**¡Canta!** *Sing!*) and the plural (**¡Cantad!** *Sing!*). There are separate forms for the formal imperative, which uses the third-person subjunctive (singular and plural).

- To address one person formally, the imperative is the same as the third-person singular present subjunctive (i.e. **-e** for **-ar** verbs or **-a** for **-er** and **-ir** verbs):

  ¡Cante! *Sing!* (**cantar**) **¡Coma!** *Eat!* (**comer**) **¡Abra!** *Open!* (**abrir**)

- To address more than one person formally, the imperative is the third-person plural present subjunctive (i.e. **-en** for **-ar** verbs or **-an** for **-er** and **-ir** verbs):

  ¡Canten! *Sing!*   **¡Coman!** *Eat!*   **¡Abran!** *Open!*

- The formal object pronoun for reflexive verbs is the third-person **se**:

  ¡Siéntese, señora! *Sit down, madam!*
  ¡Siéntense, señoras! *Sit down, ladies!*

9 For each of these commands, indicate the form of address used.

	Tratamiento de tú	Tratamiento de usted
a. ¡Venid a visitar España!	☐	☐
b. ¡Aprenda a hablar español!	☐	☐
c. ¡Diviértase en nuestras discotecas!	☐	☐
d. ¡Bañaos en nuestras playas!	☐	☐

10 Write four commands for each of these signs: informal singular, informal plural, formal singular and formal plural.

Hacer deporte

a. ....

b. ....

c. ....

d. ....

Tener cuidado con el perro

e. ....

f. ....

g. ....

h. ....

Conducir lentamente

i. ....

j. ....

k. ....

l. ....

Ponerse el cinturón

m. ....

n. ....

o. ....

p. ....

¡Enhorabuena! You've reached the end of Lesson 10. It's time to count up the icons for the exercises and record your result here and in the table on page 128.

11

More on adjectives, adverbs & prepositions

Intensifiers

- To make the meaning of an adjective stronger, **muy** *very* can be used. Alternatively, the suffix **-ísimo/-a/-os/-as** can be added to the adjective. In this case, if the adjective ends in a vowel, the suffix replaces it; if it ends in a consonant, the suffix is simply added to the end of the word.

Es caro. *It's* (m.) *expensive.* → **Es muy caro.** or **Es carísimo.** *It's very expensive.*
Son altas. *They* (f.) *are tall.* → **Son muy altas.** or **Son altísimas.** *They are very tall.*
Es útil. *It's* (m.) *useful.* → **Es muy útil.** or **Es utilísimo.** *It's very useful.*

- With this suffix, if an adjective ends in **-go/-ga** or **-co/-ca** it has a spelling change to retain the original pronunciation of the final consonant.

Es simpática. → **Es simpatiquísima.**
Es amargo. → **Es amarguísimo.**

- The superlative (formed in English with the suffix *-est* or with *the most* + adjective) is formed in Spanish with **el/la/los/las** (+ noun) + **más** + adjective:

Es el más alto. *He is the tallest.*
Es el hombre más alto del mundo. *He's the tallest man in the world.*
Son las casas más caras. *They are the most expensive houses.*

1 Complete each sentence, replacing the underlined words with an adjective + intensifying suffix.

a. El Amazonas es un río <u>muy largo</u>. Es un río ....

b. En el Amazonas hay <u>muchos</u> tipos de peces. Hay .... tipos de peces.

c. Quedan <u>muy pocas</u> tribus primitivas. Quedan .... tribus primitivas.

d. Amazonia es <u>muy rica</u> en recursos naturales. Es .... en recursos naturales.

e. La deforestación es <u>muy peligrosa</u> para el planeta. Es .... para el planeta.

f. Es <u>muy importante</u> proteger Amazonia. Es .... proteger Amazonia.

② **Rephrase the following sentences as world records.**
E.g. Es una ciudad muy poblada. ➔ Es la ciudad .... del mundo.

a. México tiene veinticinco millones de habitantes: es una ciudad muy poblada.

➔ ....

b. El Amazonas mide 6.800 kilómetros: es un río muy largo.

➔ ....

c. El colibrí cubano pesa veinte gramos: es un pájaro muy ligero.

➔ ....

d. Las tortugas argentinas viven ciento cincuenta años:
son animales muy longevos.

➔ ....
....

A lot, a little / many, few

• To say how much or little you do something, you use the adverb **mucho** *a lot, much* or **poco** *little, not much* after the verb.

Trabajo mucho. *I work a lot.*
Voy poco al cine. *I don't go to the cinema much.*

It is also possible to use these adverbs with an adjective:

Me siento mucho / poco motivada. *I feel very / don't feel very motivated.*

• When used to modify a noun, **mucho/-a/-os/-as** *a lot of, much, many* and **poco/-a/-os/-as** *little, few* are adjectives and must agree in gender and number with the noun:

Como mucho / poco pescado. *I eat a lot of / little fish.*
Bebe mucha / poca cerveza. *He drinks a lot of / little beer.*
Tengo muchos / pocos amigos. *I have many / few friends.*
Escribo muchas / pocas cartas. *I write many / few letters.*

In English, **poco** often translates most naturally to the negative *don't ...*, e.g. *I don't eat much fish. I don't write many letters*, etc.

• Note that to say *a bit (of), a little (of)*, the Spanish is **un poco (de)**.

Necesito descansar un poco. *I need to rest a bit.*
Dame un poco de vino. *Give me a little wine.*

3 Tick the box that corresponds to the missing word in each sentence.

	muy	mucho	muchos	mucha	muchas
a. Me gusta .... chatear en Internet.	☐	☐	☐	☐	☐
b. Me hago .... amigos chateando.	☐	☐	☐	☐	☐
c. Me paso .... horas conectado.	☐	☐	☐	☐	☐
d. Para los niños, Internet puede ser .... peligroso.	☐	☐	☐	☐	☐
e. Hay .... información interesante en línea.	☐	☐	☐	☐	☐
f. Suelo perder .... tiempo en Internet.	☐	☐	☐	☐	☐
g. .... chicos juegan en línea.	☐	☐	☐	☐	☐
h. El juego en línea provoca .... adicción.	☐	☐	☐	☐	☐

4 Translate these sentences into Spanish using the correct form of *poco*.

a. I don't do much sport. → ....

b. You *(sing. inf.)* don't eat much fish. → ....

c. They *(m.)* are not very nice. → ....

d. We *(m.)* are not very patient. → ....

e. I don't buy many shoes. → ....

f. He doesn't eat much meat. → ....

g. You *(sing. inf.)* don't write many letters. → ....

h. This film is not very interesting. → ....

Too much, enough, quite

- When used as an adverb (i.e. with a verb or an adjective), **demasiado** *too much* and **bastante** *enough* do not change.

  Como demasiado. *I eat too much.*
  Esta niña no come bastante. *This little girl doesn't eat enough.*

- However, as adjectives (i.e. used with a noun), they change form to agree with the noun (**demasiado/-a/-os/-as** or **bastante/s**).

  Como demasiadas golosinas. *I eat too many sweets.*
  No come bastantes verduras. *He doesn't eat enough vegetables.*

- Used with an adjective (thus, as an adverb), **bastante** means *quite*, *rather* and **demasiado** means *too*.

  Está bastante delgada. *She's rather thin.*
  La sopa está demasiado fría. *The soup is too cold.*

5 Here, a mother is criticizing her son: for example, 'You play too much on the computer!' Complete the bubbles with her reprimands.

a. ¡Juegas .... a la Play Station!

b. ¡Te pasas .... horas en Internet!

c. ¡Te acuestas .... tarde!

d. ¡Tienes .... amigos!

e. ¡Soy .... paciente contigo!

f. ¡Tienes .... libertad!

6 The son tries to defend himself: 'That's not true! My grades are quite good!' Complete the bubbles with his denials.

a. ¡Mentira! ¡Mis notas son .... buenas.

b. ¡Mentira! No tengo .... amigos.

c. ¡Mentira! No eres .... paciente conmigo.

d. ¡Mentira! No tengo .... libertad.

Forming adverbs

- To form an adverb from an adjective, just add the suffix **-mente** (the equivalent of *-ly* in English) to the feminine form of the adjective. (If you need to review the feminine form of adjectives, see page 9.)

  tonto *stupid, silly*   → **tont<u>a</u>mente** *stupidly*
  fuerte *strong*   → **fuertemente** *strongly*
  feliz *happy*   → **felizmente** *happily*
  habitual *habitual*   → **habitualmente** *habitually, usually*

- When the adjective has a written accent, the adverbial form retains it.

  inútil *useless*   → **inútilmente** *uselessly*
  espléndido *splendid*   → **espléndid<u>a</u>mente** *splendidly*

7 Write the feminine form of the adjective, then use this to construct the corresponding adverb ending in *-mente*. Finally, complete the sentences below the table with the correct adverbs.

masculine	feminine	ADVERB
cariñoso		
ágil		
triste		
feroz		
cómodo		
único		

a. Este perro es muy malo: ladra .... a todos los que pasan.

b. El perro está malo: me mira ....

c. El gato duerme .... en el sofá.

d. El gato salta .... por la ventana.

e. A los gatos les gusta que les acaricien ....

f. Las jirafas viven .... en África.

Prepositions: a few difficulties

- In phrases such as *it is difficult to / important to*, etc., the preposition *to* is not included in Spanish unless the following infinitive ends the clause or sentence. In this case, the preposition **de** is used:

  Es difícil aprender las conjugaciones. *It is difficult to learn conjugations.*
  Es difícil de decir. *It is difficult to say.*

- In general the preposition **a** indicates movement, i.e. *to*, while **en** indicates location, i.e. *in* or *at*.

  Viajo a Londres. *I'm travelling to London.*   **Estoy en Londres.** *I'm in London.*
  Voy al trabajo. *I'm going to work.*   **Estoy en el trabajo.** *I'm at work.*

8 Complete these sentences with one of the options given in parentheses.

a. .... estudiar los verbos. **(Es esencial / Es esencial de)**

b. .... fumar en este bar. **(Está prohibido / Está prohibido de)**

c. Esta palabra es .... pronunciar. **(imposible / imposible de)**

d. A mí me .... aprender idiomas. **(es fácil / es fácil de)**

e. No .... recordar las conjugaciones. **(es fácil / es fácil de)**

9 Complete these sentences with *a* or *en*.

a. ...... Sevilla, la gente es muy simpática.

b. Los estudiantes que residen ...... Sevilla están muy contentos.

c. Muchos alumnos van ...... Sevilla para estudiar.

d. Cuando vuelven ...... su país, sienten nostalgia.

e. ¿Dónde estás? ¿...... casa?

f. Ven ...... casa, te invito.

Great! You've completed Lesson 11. It's time to count up the icons for the exercises and record your result here and in the table on page 128.

Taking the train

- The national rail service in Spain is called **RENFE** (**Red Nacional de Ferrocarriles Españoles** *National Network of Spanish Railways*). Several major cities are linked by a high-speed train service, the **AVE** (**Alta Velocidad Española**), whose logo is a bird (**ave** means *bird*). Travelling at 310 km/h (193 mph), **AVE** trains connect Madrid to cities including Barcelona, Valencia, Alicante, Sevilla and Málaga.

- Apart from **trenes de larga y media distancia** *long- and medium-distance trains*, there are also **cercanías** *suburban trains* (literally, 'proximities'). See the box for a few other useful words.

la estación *station*

el andén *platform*

la taquilla *ticket window*

el descuento *reduced fare*

pagar con tarjeta *to pay with a credit card*

pagar en efectivo *to pay in cash*

turista *second class*

preferente *first class*

---

renfe　　**Billete + Reserva**　　LOC.: YMM89SKD　　CQBE8890 2473

Combinado Cercanias: EAA9L　　　　　　　　　　16NOV12 19:50

VALIDEZ DE REGRESO 60 DIAS　　VCX　CQBE8890 2473　　Fecha:　17NOV12

　7419700306113　　　　　　　　　　16NOV12 19:50　　Tren:　00277

Fecha:	17NOV12		Coche:	4	TURISTA			ALM-MCH
Salida:	ALMERIA	07.05	Plaza:	6D	SENTADA		Coche:	4
Llegada:	MCHAMARTIN	13.27					Plaza:	6D
Producto:	TALGO	00277						

Fecha:		Coche:	*Firmado y conforme el cliente*	Fecha:	
Salida:		Plaza:	*los datos del billete.*	Tren:	
Llegada:					
Producto:				Coche:	
				Plaza:	

© CIT 1996

016 IDA Y VUELTA　　　　Precio　　　　: ***46,40

METALICO　　　　　　　　Gastos gestion: ****1,60　　Tarifa: 016

　　　　　　　　　　　　TOTAL:　　　　***48,00　　Total　***48,00

　　07105040464 IVA 10%　　　　**4,33　　　　　　　　@@

I Use the train ticket above to find the Spanish word for each of these terms:

a. outward journey: ....　**f.** in cash: ....　**k.** reservation: ....

b. destination: ....　**g.** fees: ....　**l.** fare: ....

c. ticket: ....　**h.** seat: ....　**m.** train: ....

d. date: ....　**i.** price: ....　**n.** sales tax: ....

e. place of departure: .....　**j.** return journey: ....　**o.** carriage: ....

En la estación

– BuenosdíasporfavormegustaunaentradaporParís.

El señor de la ventanilla abre mucho los ojos.

– ¿Qué dice?

Frank coge aire y lo intenta otra vez.

– BuenosdíasporfavorquierounaentradaparaParís.

– Oiga, esto no es un cine – contesta el empleado.

– Perdón, no entiendo.

– Digo que esto no es un cine, que aquí no puede ver películas.

– No entiendo. Perdón.

– Tiene que decir «billete». Las entradas son para el cine y para el teatro.

– Entiendo. Sí. Perdón… Por favor, quiero un billete para París.

– Así. Muy bien. ¿De ida y vuelta o sencillo?

– No entiendo.

– ¿DE IDA Y VUELTA O SENCILLO?

– No entiendo.

– Tiene que hablar más despacio y no más alto. Este chico es extranjero, no sordo. Oye muy bien – dice alguien detrás de Frank.

Alfonso Buitrago, *Por soñar*, en De viaje, Santillana, 1997.

2 Read the text *En la estación* and then tick the correct answers below.

a. En este texto, ¿cuántos protagonistas hay?

uno ☐

dos ☐

tres ☐

cuatro ☐

b. ¿Cómo habla español Frank?

Lo habla perfectamente. ☐

No habla nada de español. ☐

Lo habla pero bastante mal. ☐

c. Frank quiere:

un billete de tren para París ☐

una entrada para el cine ☐

una entrada para el teatro ☐

d. El empleado de la taquilla:

es sordo ☐

es extranjero ☐

no entiende bien a Frank ☐

3 Using the text to help you, translate the following sentences.

a. The employee *(m.)* is not deaf. → ....

b. It is necessary to speak slowly. → ....

c. I see someone behind Frank. → ....

4 Did you note the difference between *billete* and *entrada* referring to ticket?
Use the appropriate term in each sentence in the correct form (singular
or plural) and with the correct article (*el, la, los, las*) — or no article!

a. Hola, ¿vende usted .... para trenes de cercanías?

b. Cómprame dos .... para el concierto de Bisbal, por favor.

c. .... de autobús es más barato que el de tren.

d. En avión, si tienes .... de primera clase, ¡te dan champán gratis!

e. .... para las corridas de toros suelen ser bastante caras.

f. Para esta obra de teatro, puedes comprar .... en Internet.

5 This text has several examples of *oír* 'to hear' and *entender* 'to understand' —
which are not always the same thing, as the conversation makes clear!
Use the appropriate term in each sentence, conjugated in the correct person.

a. Este joven .... muy bien: no hace falta que hable tan alto.

b. Leo bien el español pero no .... a la gente cuando habla demasiado rápido.

c. Sube el volumen de la música, por favor: ¡no .... nada!

d. Este texto es demasiado difícil para mí: no .... nada.

e. ¿ .... usted lo que digo o se lo vuelvo a explicar?

f. ¡Estoy en el tren! Hay mucho ruido. ¿Me ....?

6 *El damero maldito* ('the cursed checkerboard') is a favourite of Spanish fans of word games. First find the words that match the definitions below, and then put the letters into the corresponding numbers of the checkerboard. Can you find and translate the hidden phrase?

a. Para entrar en una casa hay que abrir la…

26	2	19	32	16	29

e. Lo que cuesta una cosa es su…

30	7	17	21	12	25

b. Para abrir la puerta hace falta una…

14	23	39	40	6

f. Sirve para sentarse, es la…

34	3	24	13	31

c. Los hijos de mi hermano son mis…

18	36	11	42	22	20	41	4

g. Animal muy fiel (en femenino):

35	15	28	37	8

d. Adverbio de lugar que indica proximidad:

27	1	9	33

h. Indica que algo termina:

38	5	10

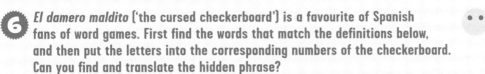

1	2	3	4	5	6	7
8	■	9	10	■	11	12
13	14	15	16	17	■	18
19	20	21	22	23	24	25
■	26	27	28	29	■	30
31	32	33	34	■	35	36
37	■	38	39	40	41	42

i. La frase escondida es:

....
....
....
....

j. Y su traducción es:

....
....
....
....

Asking for directions

Spaniards have the reputation of being very helpful when asked for directions. Although it's a bit of a cliché, it's often said that if you are trying to find your way somewhere, they may well accompany you to your destination!

All the same, ideally it's best to be able to ask questions clearly and understand any explanations you're given.

To ask questions:

¿Puede(s) decirme...
Can you (formal / inf.) *tell me ...*
... dónde está / dónde queda...?
... where ... is?
... cómo se va a...?
... how to get to...?

To give directions:

ir a / hasta *to go to / as far as*
seguir *to continue*
girar *to turn*
tomar *to take*
a la derecha *on the right*
a la izquierda *on the left*
recto *straight on*
la primera / segunda / tercera
the first, second, third

7 Read the four exchanges next to the map on page 79 and indicate for each one if formal or informal address is used.

	Tú	Usted
a.	☐	☐
b.	☐	☐
c.	☐	☐
d.	☐	☐

9 A man leaving the cinema wants to go to the library and asks a woman for directions. Write their exchange below using informal address (a question and a reply, as on page 79).

8 Use the information on page 79 to give the name of the street on which each place below is found.

a. El colegio está
→ ....

b. La biblioteca está
→ ....

c. La discoteca está
→ ....

d. El cine está
→ ....

– ....
....
....
....

– ....
....
....
....
....

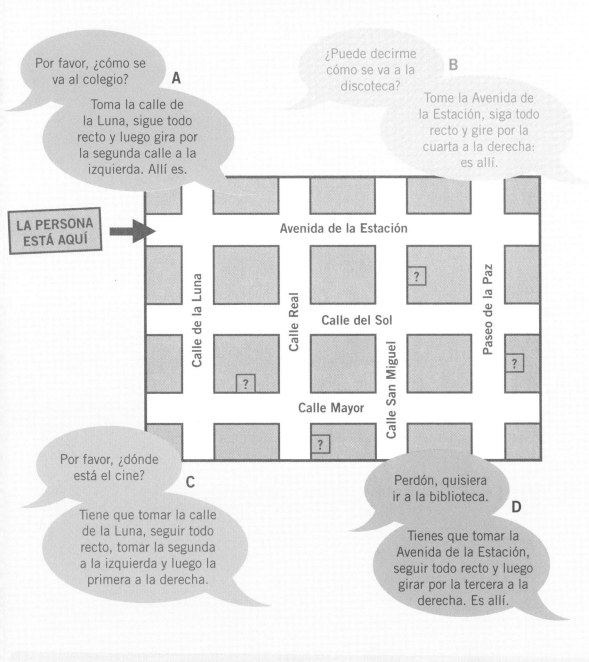

Por favor, ¿cómo se va al colegio? **A**

Toma la calle de la Luna, sigue todo recto y luego gira por la segunda calle a la izquierda. Allí es.

¿Puede decirme cómo se va a la discoteca? **B**

Tome la Avenida de la Estación, siga todo recto y gire por la cuarta a la derecha: es allí.

LA PERSONA ESTÁ AQUÍ

Avenida de la Estación

Calle de la Luna

Calle Real

Calle del Sol

Paseo de la Paz

Calle San Miguel

Calle Mayor

Por favor, ¿dónde está el cine? **C**

Tiene que tomar la calle de la Luna, seguir todo recto, tomar la segunda a la izquierda y luego la primera a la derecha.

Perdón, quisiera ir a la biblioteca. **D**

Tienes que tomar la Avenida de la Estación, seguir todo recto y luego girar por la tercera a la derecha. Es allí.

¡Estupendo! You've completed Vocabulary and Comprehension 2. It's time to count up the icons for the exercises and record your result here and in the table on page 128.

12
The future & relative clauses

Two ways to express the future

- The near future (conveying something that is going to happen soon) is formed with a verb phrase that is very similar to the English: **ir** *to go* (conjugated) + **a** + infinitive:

Voy a comer. *I'm going to eat.*
¿Vas a venir? *Are you going to come?*
Vamos a hacer un viaje. *We're going to take a trip.*

cantar (regular)	poder (irregular)
cantaré	podré
cantarás	podrás
cantará	podrá
cantaremos	podremos
cantaréis	podréis
cantarán	podrán

- There is also a future tense, which in Spanish is formed by adding conjugation endings to the infinitive (unlike in English, which uses the auxiliary verb *will*): e.g. **comeré** (**comer** + **é**) *I will eat.* See the box for the endings, which are the same in all three verb groups (**-ar**, **-er** and **-ir**). Pay attention to the written accents, which indicate the stress is on the last syllable.

- There are just 12 irregular verbs in the future tense. The irregularity occurs in the stem:

caber: cabré, etc.   **poder: podré,** etc.   **salir: saldré,** etc.
decir: diré, etc.   **poner: pondré,** etc.   **tener: tendré,** etc.
haber: habré, etc.   **querer: querré,** etc. **valer: valdré,** etc.
hacer: haré, etc.   **saber: sabré,** etc.   **venir: vendré,** etc.

1 Underline the seven verbs in the future tense in this brief extract from a novel, then write them out followed by their infinitive.

a. future: .... /
   infinitive: ....

b. future: .... /
   infinitive: ....

c. future: .... /
   infinitive: ....

d. future: .... /
   infinitive: ....

– Si tú quieres, yo haré de ti un gran guitarrista.

– Pero si no tengo tiempo ni guitarra.

– Yo te regalaré una guitarra. Y en cuanto al tiempo, déjalo también de mi cuenta. También tengo algunos remedios para eso. Junto con la guitarra, te voy a regalar tiempo para tocarla. Serás guitarrista en unos pocos meses. Harás viajes, ganarás dinero, seducirás mujeres, y nunca tendrás jefe.

Luis Landero, El guitarrista, Tusquets Editores, Barcelona, 2002.

e. future: .... / infinitive: ....

f. future: .... / infinitive: ....

g. future: .... / infinitive: ....

2 Conjugate the first two verbs in the text in all persons of the future tense.

a.

....

....

....

....

....

....

b.

....

....

....

....

....

....

3 Rewrite the following sentences, replacing the near future (*ir a* + infinitive) with the future tense.

a. ¿Me vas a ayudar a tocar la guitarra?

➜ ....

b. Vamos a ser famosos. ➜ ....

c. No voy a poder tocar esta partitura.

➜ ....

d. Me vais a decir qué os parece esta guitarra.

➜ ....

e. El público va a querer que sigas tocando.

➜ ....

f. No van a tener tiempo para aprender. ➜ ....

Indicative or subjunctive?

- In most cases, the future is used in much the same way as in English, often with the present indicative:

Mañana <u>trabajaré</u>. *I will work tomorrow.*
Te <u>ayudaré</u> si tengo tiempo. *I will help you if I have time.*
No sé si <u>podré</u> salir. *I don't know if I'll be able to go out.*
¿Sabes cuándo <u>vendrás</u>? *Do you know when you will come?*
Pienso que <u>volveré</u>. *I think that I will return.*

- However, in subordinate clauses introduced by words to do with time, such as **cuando** *when, whenever,* **en cuanto** *as soon as,* **mientras** *while, as long as,* etc., the subjunctive is required in that clause because the action has yet to occur. The main clause is in the future (or as in the third example, the imperative):

Cuando pueda [subj.]**, <u>iré</u> a verte.** *Whenever I can, I will come to see you.*
Te <u>ayudaré</u> mientras quieras [subj.]**.** *I will help you as long as you wish.*
En cuanto tengas [subj.] **dinero, ¡págame!** *As soon as you have money, pay me!*
El día que vengas [subj.]**, <u>saldremos</u> a pasear.** *On the day that you come, we'll go out for a walk.*

4 Translate the following sentences.

a. I wonder if they will come. ➜ ....

b. As soon as I see you *(sing. inf.)*, I will pay you. ➜ ....

c. He doesn't know if he will be able to come. ➜ ....

d. Do you *(sing. inf.)* know when her book will come out? ➜ ....

e. He asks himself where he will live. ➜ ....

f. The day when I pay you *(sing. inf.)*, you will be happy. ➜ ....

g. I don't know if we will sing. ➜ ....

h. I don't know how I'll dress. ➜ ....

i. I'll read his book when it comes out. ➜ ....

j. As soon as it's sunny, I'll go to the beach. ➜ ....

5 Rewrite the following sentences to talk about the future, using a subordinate clause with a time word.

E.g. I'm not going to Mexico because I don't speak Spanish well.
→ When I speak Spanish well, I will go to Mexico.

a. No voy a México porque no hablo bien español.

Cuando .... español, ... a México.

b. No conduzco una moto porque no soy mayor de edad.

Cuando .... mayor de edad, ... una moto.

c. No sabes las conjugaciones porque no las aprendes.

Cuando las ...., ... las conjugaciones.

d. Este chico no tiene buenas notas porque no estudia.

Cuando ...., este chico .... buenas notas.

e. No van a la playa porque no hace sol.

Cuando .... sol, ... a la playa.

Using the future to make a conjecture

- In Spanish, the future tense can also be used to make conjectures about the present. This is usually expressed in English with *perhaps*, *probably*, *I think*, etc.

  Serán las ocho. *It must be 8:00.*
  Estará viendo la tele. *Perhaps he's watching television.*
  Vendrá tarde. *She's probably coming late.* (or *She will be coming late.*)

- Thus there are three ways of making a conjecture in Spanish: the present indicative, the future indicative and the subjunctive.

  A lo mejor piensa que tengo dinero. *Perhaps he thinks that I have money.*
  Pensará que tengo dinero. *He must think that I have money.*
  Tal vez (or **quizás**) **piense que tengo dinero.** *Maybe he thinks that I have money.*

6 Translate the following sentences.

a. La persona que usted busca no vive aquí: será un error.

→ ....

b. Pedro ha llamado diez veces: querrá decirte algo importante.

→ ....

7 Rephrase each underlined conjecture in two different ways.

Dice que no puede salir esta noche. <u>A lo mejor está repasando un examen.</u>

a. .... un examen.

b. .... un examen.

Lo he llamado pero no contesta. <u>Quizás no tiene cobertura el móvil.</u>

c. .... cobertura el móvil.

d. .... cobertura el móvil.

Lleva zapatillas de deporte y un chándal. <u>Irá al gimnasio.</u>

e. ....al gimnasio.

f. ....al gimnasio.

Relative clauses

A relative clause gives more information about a previously mentioned noun, using a word such as *that*, *which*, *who*, etc. In English, the relative pronoun can often be left out, but in Spanish it must be included.

- **que** *that*, *which*, *who*, etc. is the most common relative pronoun in Spanish sentences. It can refer to either people or things.

  El hombre que canta. *The man who is singing.*
  El disco que escucho. *The disc (that) I'm listening to.*

- Another possibility is to use a preposition + **el/la/los/las que** or **el/la/los/las cual/cuales** (for either people or things) or **quien/quienes** (only for people). In these cases the form needs to agree with the gender and number of the noun.

  La empresa en la que trabajo. *The company in which I work.*
  Las personas con las que trabajo. *The people with whom I work.*
  El hombre a / de quien hablo. *The man to / of whom I'm speaking.*
  uno de los cuales... *one* (m.) *of which ...*

- To give information about location or time, **donde** *where*, **cuando** *when* or **en que** *in/on which* are possible:

  El día en que nací. *The day on which I was born.*
  El año cuando nací. *The year (when) I was born.*
  El país en que vivo. *The country in which I live.*
  La ciudad donde resido. *The town where I live.*

8 **Link the two sentences using a relative clause.**
E.g. I'm speaking to ('addressing') a woman. This woman is my teacher.
→ The woman to whom I'm speaking is my teacher.

a. Me dirijo a una mujer. Esta mujer es mi profesora.

.... es mi profesora.

b. Vivo en un barrio. Este barrio es muy simpático.

.... es muy simpático.

c. Reparto pizzas con una moto. Esta moto es verde.

.... es verde.

d. Te hablo de una chica. Esta chica es mi vecina.

.... es mi vecina.

9 **Complete these sentences with the appropriate relative pronoun (*donde/cuando* or *en que*). If there is more than one possibility, write them both, separated by /.**

a. La ciudad .... se pasan las vacaciones está a la orilla del mar.

b. Me acuerdo muy bien de la noche .... te conocí.

c. ¿Cuál fue el año .... el Barça ganó la Champions?

d. Esta es la casa .... me gustaría vivir.

10 **For each sentence, underline the verb(s) in the subjunctive. Then translate it into English.**

a. Ven cuando puedas.

→ ....

b. El primero que me llame tendrá un coche.

→ ....

c. El día que vengas, estaré contento.

→ ....

d. Querré al hombre que me entienda.

→ ....

Well done! You've reached the end of Lesson 12. It's time to count up the icons for the exercises and record your result here and in the table on page 128.

13
Talking about the past

The imperfect

- The imperfect is used to express a regular, repeated action or a continuous description in the past. It often translates to *was/were ...-ing* or *used to +* infinitive.

- It is formed by replacing the infinitive ending with **-aba** for **-ar** verbs and **-ía** for **-er** and **-ir** verbs.

- Only three verbs are irregular in the imperfect:

  ser: era, eras, era, éramos, erais, eran
  ir: iba, ibas, iba, íbamos, ibais, iban
  ver: veía, veías, veía, veíamos, veíais, veían

cantar	comer
cantaba	comía
cantabas	comías
cantaba	comía
cantábamos	comíamos
cantabais	comíais
cantaban	comían

 1 Complete this table of imperfect conjugations with the missing verb forms.

INFINITIVE	yo	tú	él, ella, usted	nosotros, nosotras	vosotros, vosotras	ellos, ellas, ustedes
		jugabas		jugábamos		jugaban
estar	estaba		estaba		estabais	
hacer	hacía	hacías	hacía			
				decíamos	decíais	decían
divertirse	me	te				

2 Complete these sentences, conjugating the verb in the imperfect.

a. En mi época, yo no .... (ir) tanto al cine.

b. Cuando .... (tener) quince años, yo no .... (ser) tan libre.

c. Cuando .... (ser) pequeños, nosotros no .... (ver) tanto la tele.

d. Los mayores .... (oír) la radio y los niños .... (jugar) en la calle.

3 Complete this text with the appropriate forms of *ser* or *estar* in the imperfect.

Toda la familia .... en el salón: .... la hora de la comida y todos ....

viendo la tele. A veces, los padres y los hijos no .... de acuerdo: unos ....

partidarios de ver las series y otros .... a favor del telediario. Pero el padre siempre

.... de mal humor y además .... muy autoritario, de modo que siempre

.... él quien decidía.

The preterite

- The preterite is used to express a completed action in the past, translating to the simple past in English (the past tense that typically ends in *-ed*):

  Ayer cené en un restaurant. *Yesterday I dined in a restaurant.*

  Note the difference with the imperfect:

  Cenaba en aquel restaurant. *I used to dine in that restaurant. / I was dining in that restaurant ...*

cantar	comer
canté	comí
cantaste	comiste
cantó	comió
cantamos	comimos
cantasteis	comisteis
cantaron	comieron

- It is formed by replacing the infinitive ending with the endings below. Pay attention to the written accents: they indicate the stressed syllable, which is important to avoid confusion with other tenses.

  -ar verbs ➔ **-é, -aste, -ó, -amos, -asteis, -aron**
  -er and **-ir** verbs ➔ **-í, -iste, -ió, -imos, -isteis, -ieron**

- In verbs ending in **-gar** or **-car**, the first-person singular in the preterite undergoes a spelling change to retain the same pronunciation: e.g. **jugar ➔ jugué** *I played*, **indicar ➔ indiqué** *I indicated*. Otherwise, the conjugation is regular.

4 Here are 15 conjugated forms of the verbs *pagar*, *escribir*, *jugar*, *contar*, *cerrar* and *beber*. Cross out the ones that are not preterite forms.

pagué   escribe   contó   cerró   contamos

cerraron   escribimos   bebí   bebemos   contéis

juegue   escribiste   pagasteis   cierro   bebió

5 Find three verbs in the preterite in this grid (vertically, horizontally or diagonally). Circle them and then give their full conjugation in the preterite.

V	T	L	E	Ó	N	T	E
T	O	M	I	E	R	O	N
B	A	L	P	E	N	S	É
A	M	I	V	U	A	S	O
I	I	L	I	I	E	T	E
L	C	Y	V	G	S	U	R
I	H	C	I	U	R	T	U
Ó	U	T	Ó	E	L	L	E

a. ....

....

....

....

....

....

b. ....

....

....

....

....

....

c. ....

....

....

....

....

....

6 Complete these sentences with the appropriate preterite form.
E.g. El año pasado no XXX, pero este año voy a estudiar.
→ El año pasado no estudié, pero este año voy a estudiar.

a. El año pasado no XXX en casa, pero este año vas a ayudar.

→ ....

b. El curso pasado no XXX, pero este año voy a leer.

→ ....

c. El año pasado XXX mucho tiempo en Internet, pero este año no vais a perder tanto.

→ ....

d. El año pasado mi hermano XXX mucho al fútbol, pero este año no va a jugar tanto.

→ ....

7 Connect each situation on the left with the most likely outcome on the right, as in the example.

a. no saber la respuesta •
b. la puerta / estar cerrada •
c. no quedar café •
d. María / no contestar al teléfono •
e. no haber billetes de avión •
f. no tener ganas de salir •
g. el ascensor / no funcionar •
h. el título / parecer interesante •
i. yo / querer trabajar en Madrid •
j. el programa / no ser interesante •

• subir por las escaleras
• decidir ver una serie en la tele
• no escribir nada
• aprender español
• llamar a su puerta
• entrar por la ventana
• apagar la tele
• preparar un té
• viajar en tren
• abrir el libro

8 Now write the corresponding sentences in the past. Remember that the imperfect is used to describe a situation, and the preterite to express a completed action.

a. **Como no** <u>sabía</u> **la respuesta, no** <u>escribí</u> **nada.**

b. → ....

c. → ....

d. → ....

e. → ....

f. → ....

g. → ....

h. → ....

i. → ....

j. → ....

The present perfect

cantar	comer
he cantado	he comido
has cantado	has comido
ha cantado	ha comido
hemos cantado	hemos comido
habéis cantado	habéis comido
han cantado	han comido

- The present perfect is used to describe a recent completed action, i.e. when the past event is still considered to be current (in reality or in perception). It is the equivalent of *have/has ...-ed*, but can also sometimes translate to the English simple past.

- It is composed of the auxiliary verb **haber** *to have* (conjugated) + past participle, which is formed by replacing the infinitive ending with **-ado** for **-ar** verbs, and **-ido** for **-er** and **-ir** verbs.

Ya he tomado café, gracias. *I have already had coffee, thank you.*
Hemos dormido muy bien. *We slept really well.*
Todavía no hemos salido. *We haven't left yet.*

- There are quite a few irregular past participles. Here are a few common ones:

abierto (abrir)	**dicho (decir)**	**escrito (escribir)**	**hecho (hacer)**
puesto (poner)	**roto (romper)**	**visto (ver)**	**vuelto (volver)**

 **Rewrite these sentences using the present perfect.**

a. Yo no abro la puerta.

→ ....

b. Volvéis de las vacaciones cansados.

→ ....

c. ¿Le escribes a la abuela?

→ ....

d. No podemos venir a tu cumpleaños.

→ ....

e. ¿Ustedes piden pescado?

→ ....

10 Put each of these six verbs in the present perfect into the appropriate sentence.

a. No encuentro las llaves: ¿dónde las ....?

b. No estoy contento contigo: no .... tus deberes.

c. ¿Quién .... mis gafas?

d. Te .... mil veces que no te pases horas con el ordenador.

e. Muchas gracias por la invitación: .... muy bien.

f. Te .... Carmen y Juan.

ha visto

hemos comido

he dicho

han llamado

habéis puesto

has hecho

11 Which of these things have you already done (*ya...*) or not yet done (*todavía no...*)? Tick the appropriate box and then write the corresponding sentence.

	Sí	No	
a. viajar en avión	☐	▣	Todavía no he viajado en avión.
b. comer paella	▣	☐	Ya he comido paella.
c. ver una película española en VO	☐	☐	....
d. hacer autoestop	☐	☐	....
e. cantar flamenco	☐	☐	....
f. tener un diario íntimo	☐	☐	....
g. estar enamorado/-a	☐	☐	....
h. bañarse en el Atlántico	☐	☐	....
i. hacer un discurso	☐	☐	....
j. subir en globo	☐	☐	....
k. actuar en una obra teatral	☐	☐	....
l. ir a América latina	☐	☐	....

¡Genial! You've completed Lesson 13. It's time to count up the icons for the exercises and record your results here and in the table on page 128.

14
More about tenses

Verbs that are irregular in the preterite

- A number of frequently used verbs are irregular in the preterite. Most share the same irregular endings in the first- and third-person singular: **-e**, **-iste**, **-o**, **-imos**, **-isteis**, **-ieron**. Unlike regular preterite endings, these do not have a written accent.

- The stem of these verbs is also irregular: see the box for the forms of **estar**. The other irregular stems follow this model.

estar	other irregular stems	
estuv<u>e</u>	anduv- (andar)	quis- (querer)
estuv<u>iste</u>	cup- (caber)	sup- (saber)
estuv<u>o</u>	hic- (hacer)	traj- (traer)
estuv<u>imos</u>	hub- (haber)	tuv- (tener)
estuv<u>isteis</u>	pud- (poder)	vin- (venir)
estuv<u>ieron</u>	pus- (poner)	

- There are also some uniquely irregular verbs:

  - **decir** in the third-person plural ends in **-eron**: **dije, dijiste, dijo, dijimos, dijisteis, dijeron**

- **ser** and **ir** share the same conjugation: **fui, fuiste, fue, fuimos, fuisteis, fueron**.

1 Find six preterite verbs in this grid (vertically, horizontally or diagonally), then put them into the appropriate sentence.

V	I	N	I	S	T	E	I	S
P	H	I	L	T	O	R	F	A
I	U	P	B	R	A	Z	Y	T
T	E	D	I	J	I	S	T	E
O	B	L	I	L	C	H	U	S
H	R	U	T	E	S	O	V	I
I	M	A	L	L	R	H	E	J
Z	U	F	U	I	M	O	S	T
O	Q	U	O	T	N	A	N	I

a. A los diez años .... mi primera bicicleta.

b. Eres una mentirosa: ¿por qué no me .... la verdad?

c. ¿Por qué no .... a mi cumpleaños?

d. Ayer .... bastante sol.

e. Había demasiada gente y no .... entrar en el estadio.

f. La semana pasada .... a ver a la abuela.

Other irregularities in the preterite

- The -**ir** verbs with a stem change from **e → i** or **o → u** take this change in the third-person singular and plural of the preterite: **pedir → pidió, pidieron; sentir → sintió, sintieron; dormir → durmió, durmieron**.

- In verbs whose stem ends in a vowel, the initial -**i** of the preterite ending changes to -**y** in the third-person singular and plural: **leer → leyó, leyeron**.

- Verbs ending in -**ducir** have a spelling change to -**duj-** in the preterite, followed by the irregular preterite endings (p. 92): **conducir → conduje**, etc.

- Another uniquely irregular verb in the preterite is **dar** *to give*: **di, diste, dio, dimos, disteis, dieron**.

2 Rewrite these sentences using the preterite.

a. Cristóbal Colón descubre América pero no es él quien le da su nombre al Nuevo Mundo.

➔ ....

b. Mide mal la circunferencia de la Tierra, por eso el viaje dura más de lo previsto.

➔ ....

c. Repite el viaje a América cuatro veces y muere en Valladolid.

➔ ....

d. Los españoles introducen nuevas enfermedades en América.

➔ ....

e. Destruyen las antiguas culturas precolombinas y construyen otra civilización.

➔ ....

Expressing simultaneous action

- To talk about two actions that occurred at the same time in the past, one possibility is **cuando** + preterite. In Spanish, it is also very common to use **al** + infinitive:

Cuando entró or **Al entrar, vio que no había nadie.**
When he entered or *On entering, he saw that no one was there.*

3 Replace *al* + infinitive with *cuando* + preterite.

a. Al abrir el periódico, fui directamente a la página de deportes.

→ .... , fui directamente a la página de deportes.

b. Al llegar a México, noté que el acento era diferente del de España.

→ .... , noté que el acento era diferente del de España.

c. Al ver que no hacía sol, decidimos quedarnos en casa.

→ .... , decidimos quedarnos en casa.

4 Replace *cuando* + preterite with *al* + infinitive.

a. Cuando volvió a casa, el padre vio que su hijo estaba escuchando música.

→ .... , el padre vio que su hijo estaba escuchando música.

b. Cuando oyeron ruido, miraron por la ventana.

→ ...., miraron por la ventana.

c. Cuando murió, dejó todo su dinero a una ONG ('NGO').

→ ...., dejó todo su dinero a una ONG.

Saying when something happened

- Some useful time words: **hoy** *today*, **ayer** *yesterday*, **anteayer** / **antes de ayer** *the day before yesterday*, **mañana** *tomorrow*, **pasado mañana** *the day after tomorrow*, **esta mañana** *this morning*, **esta tarde** *this afternoon*, **esta noche** *tonight*.

- Remember that when talking about the past, the imperfect is used to describe something (e.g. context), while the preterite reports a specific event:

  Era [imperfect] **tarde cuando llegó** [preterite]. *It was late when she arrived.*
  Llamé [preterite] **mientras tú trabajabas** [imperfect]. *I called while you were working.*

Esta mañana he encargado libros para Candela y esta tarde voy a ayudar a Isa con la tarea de la escuela.

C

Mañana mandaré invitaciones para la presentación de Carla.

D

Ayer llamé a la distribuidora.

B

Antes de ayer llevé a Alejandro a la guardería.

A

Pasado mañana pediré el material de papelería a la distribuidora.

E

5 It's 2:00 pm on a Wednesday. Belén, a bookseller, is talking about her week: both what's happened so far and what's to come. Read what she says and list the tenses that are used below.

a. To talk about what she did on the previous days, Belén uses ....

b. To talk about what she did that morning, Belén uses ....

c. To talk about what she is going to do that afternoon, Belén uses ....

d. To talk about what she will do in the coming days, Belén uses ....

Lunes

9 h:
Llevar a Alejandro a la guardería.

14 h:
Comer con don Andrés.

22 h:
Ir al cine con Pepa y Emilia.

Martes

10 h:
Llamar a la distribuidora.

13 h:
Traer los pedidos a la tienda.

21 h:
Escribir a Carlota.

Miércoles

10 h:
Encargar libros para Candela.

11 h:
Ir al médico.

16 h:
Ayudar a Isa con la tarea de la escuela.

17 h:
Despedirme de Pedro.

Jueves

12 h:
Mandar invitaciones para la presentación de Carla.

17 h-18 h:
Dar un paseo en bici con Isa.

23 h:
Poner en el facebook las recomendaciones del librero.

Viernes

14 h:
Pedir el material de papelería a la distribuidora.

21 h:
Hacer la mochila de Isa para la excursión.

22 h:
¡Salir con Juan Carlos!

6 Recount Belén's week following these instructions: (a) Complete each sentence with two activities taken from the appropriate day or time in her diary (p. 95). (b) Write the sentences in the third-person singular (i.e. narrating what Belen did). (c) Take 2:00 pm on Wednesday as your reference point and use the tenses accordingly.

a. Antes de ayer, Belén ....

....

b. Ayer, Belén ....

....

c. Esta mañana, Belén ....

y esta tarde, ...

d. Mañana, Belén ....

....

e. Pasado mañana, Belén ....

....

The conditional

- In Spanish the conditional is formed by adding conjugation endings to the infinitive (unlike in English, which uses the auxiliary verb *would*): e.g. **comería** (**comer** + **ía**) *I would eat.* See the box for the endings, which are the same in all three verb groups (**-ar**, **-er** and **-ir**). Pay attention to the written accents, which indicate the stress is on the initial **i** of the ending.

  comería
  comerías
  comería
  comeríamos
  comeríais
  comerían

- The irregular verbs are the same as those of the future tense.

  - **caber: cabría,** etc.
  - **decir: diría,** etc.
  - **haber: habría,** etc.
  - **hacer: haría,** etc.
  - **poder: podría,** etc.
  - **poner: pondría,** etc.
  - **querer: querría,** etc.
  - **saber: sabría,** etc.
  - **salir: saldría,** etc.
  - **tener: tendría,** etc.
  - **valer: valdría,** etc.
  - **venir: vendría,** etc.

- As in English, the conditional can be used to soften a statement or make a request more polite. It can also be used with the imperfect to express the future from the perspective of the past:

  ¿Tendrías fuego? *Would you have a light?*
  Pensaba que me llamarías. *I thought that you would call me.*

7 Rephrase these sentences, using the conditional to soften them.

a. ¿Puedo utilizar tu móvil? → ....

b. ¿Es posible vernos más tarde? → ....

c. Deseamos un móvil más barato. → ....

d. ¿Estáis dispuestos a ayudarnos? → ....

e. ¿Me haces un favor? → ....

f. ¿Me dices la respuesta? → ....

8 Rewrite these sentences, using the imperfect for the verb in the main clause and the conditional for the verb in the subordinate clause.

a. Estos niños piensan que de mayores serán futbolistas.

→ ....

b. ¿Te imaginas que un día tendrás nietos?

→ ....

c. El profesor dice que pronto sabremos hablar español.

→ ....

d. Mi abuelo cree que los extraterrestres nos invadirán.

→ ....

e. Estoy convencido de que me hará este favor.

→ ....

¡Bien hecho! You've completed Lesson 14. It's time to count up the icons for the exercises and record your results here and in the table on page 128.

15

Tense sequence & conditions

The imperfect subjunctive

- We've seen that the subjunctive mood has three tenses in Spanish. The imperfect subjunctive is used to express wish, possibility, etc. in the past. It is formed using the third-person plural of the preterite (e.g. **hablaron**, **comieron**, **quisieron**) as a base, but replacing the last syllable with the endings **-ra, -ras, -ra, -ramos, -rais, -ran**.

hablar	comer	querer
hablara	comiera	quisiera
hablaras	comieras	quisieras
hablara	comiera	quisiera
habláramos	comiéramos	quisiéramos
hablarais	comierais	quisierais
hablaran	comieran	quisieran

- There is also an alternative form of the imperfect subjunctive that ends in **-se**: **hablase, hablases, hablase, hablásemos, hablaseis, hablasen**.

- The imperfect subjunctive should be used in contexts requiring the subjunctive that refer to the past. So if the verb in the main clause is in the past tense and the subordinate clause requires the subjunctive, the imperfect subjunctive is used:

Quiero (present indicative) **que vengas** (present subjunctive). *I want you to come.*
Quería (imperfect) **que vinieras** (imperfect subjunctive). *I wanted you to come.*

- The imperfect subjunctive is always required after **como si** *as if*, no matter what tense the sentence is in.

Hace como si trabajara. *He's acting as if he were working.*

1 Complete the first table by adding the third-person plural preterite forms, then use these to form the imperfect subjunctive conjugations for the three verbs.

Preterite				Imperfect subjunctive		
pedir	leer	tener		pedir	leer	tener
pedí	leí	tuve				
pediste	leíste	tuviste				
pidió	leyó	tuvo				
pedimos	leímos	tuvimos				
pedisteis	leísteis	tuvisteis				

2 Complete these sentences using the correct tense sequence (the sentence starters are in the present tense).

a. Te llamé para que vinieras a ayudarme.

Te llamo para que ....

b. Quería que alguien me dijera cómo usar este programa.

Quiero que alguien me ....

c. Le pedí al servicio técnico que me explicara lo que pasaba.

Le pido al servicio técnico que ....

d. Me dijeron que ojalá fuera solo un problema material.

Me dicen que ojalá ....

e. Yo les dije que tal vez tuviera algún virus el ordenador.

Yo les digo que tal vez ....

3 Complete these sentences using the correct tense sequence (the sentence starters are in the past tense).

a. No hace falta que compres el pan.

No hacía falta que ....

b. Te doy dinero para que vayas a hacer la compra.

Te di dinero para que ....

c. No quiero que vuelvas a traer chorizo.

No quería que ....

d. No creo que necesitemos más vino.

No creía que ....

e. Te pido sobre todo que pienses en el chocolate.

Te pedí sobre todo que ....

....

4 Complete the sentences based on the statement given.

E.g. I don't like the cinema. ➜ I act as if I loved the cinema.

a. No me gusta el cine. ➜ Hago como si .... el cine.

b. No se acordaba de mí. ➜ Hizo como si .... de mí.

c. Los niños no duermen. ➜ Hacen como si ....

d. No sabe la respuesta. ➜ Hace como si .... la respuesta.

Conditional ('if') sentences

• A 'real' conditional (to describe something possible that depends on a condition) uses the following tense sequence: the present indicative in the subordinate 'if' clause and the future indicative in the main clause (these can be in either order):

Si tengo tiempo, pasaré a verte. *If I have time, I'll come by to see you.*

• An 'unreal' conditional (to express something that is contrary to fact) uses the imperfect subjunctive in the 'if' clause and the conditional in the main clause:

Si tuviera tiempo, pasaría a verte. *If I had the time, I would come by to see you.*

5 From the 16 verbs below, circle four that are in the imperfect subjunctive and four that are in the conditional.

hiciera   costaría   hacía   conduzcas   oyeras

íbamos   encantará   habría   pusieran   oirás   habrá

pusieron   iríamos   costará   condujeras   encantaría

6 Complete these sentences using the eight verbs that you circled.

a. Si todos se .... el cinturón de seguridad, ... menos accidentes graves.

b. Si .... mejor tiempo, ... a la playa.

c. Si .... más despacio, el coche te .... menos en gasolina.

d. Si .... cómo toca la guitarra, te ....

7 *Ser* or *estar*? Complete these sentences with the imperfect subjunctive form of the appropriate verb for 'to be'.

a. No es mayor de edad. Hace como si .... mayor de edad.

b. Si Pedro .... aquí, nos ayudaría.

c. No duerme, hace como si .... durmiendo.

d. Si no .... tan cansado, te acompañaría.

e. Si .... de mejor humor, iría al cine.

f. ¡Aprender chino! Como si .... tan fácil.

8 Form 'unreal' conditional sentences by linking the conditions in table A with the most logical contrary-to-fact outcomes in table B. Use the first-person singular: *If I were sick, ...*

A	B
estar enfermo •	• mandarte mensajes
saber de informática •	• subir a las pirámides
tener tu número de móvil •	• estar más relajado
visitar México •	• cruzar la Pampa a caballo
vivir en Argentina •	• no tener problemas con el ordenador
dormir más •	• ir al médico

a. Si ....

b. Si ....

c. Si ....

d. Si ....

e. Si ....

f. Si ....

Concession clauses

- There are several ways to introduce a concession clause in English: *although, even if, even though*, etc. In Spanish, **aunque** can translate to any of these. The following verb appears in either the indicative or the subjunctive, depending on whether the action is real or hypothetical:

Aunque llueve (present indicative), **salgo.** *Though it's raining, I'm going out.* (real)
Aunque llueva (present subjunctive), **saldré.**
Even if it rains, I will go out. (hypothetical)

- A concession can also express something that is contrary to fact. In this case, the tense sequence must be the imperfect subjunctive in the subordinate concession clause and the conditional in the main clause.

Aunque lloviera, saldría. *Even if it were to rain, I would go out.*
Aunque tuviera dinero, no te daría. *Even if I had money, I wouldn't give you any.*

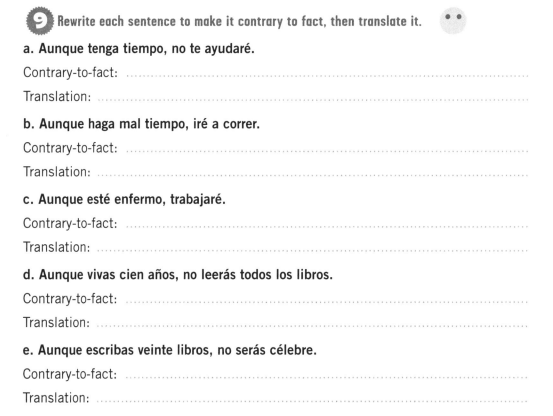

9 Rewrite each sentence to make it contrary to fact, then translate it.

a. Aunque tenga tiempo, no te ayudaré.

Contrary-to-fact: ....

Translation: ....

b. Aunque haga mal tiempo, iré a correr.

Contrary-to-fact: ....

Translation: ....

c. Aunque esté enfermo, trabajaré.

Contrary-to-fact: ....

Translation: ....

d. Aunque vivas cien años, no leerás todos los libros.

Contrary-to-fact: ....

Translation: ....

e. Aunque escribas veinte libros, no serás célebre.

Contrary-to-fact: ....

Translation: ....

Whatever, whichever, wherever, etc.

- The equivalent of *whatever, wherever, no matter what/how/who/where*, etc. is formed in Spanish by repeating the same verb in the subjunctive before and after an adverb of time, place, manner, kind or identity:

  Vengas cuando vengas... *Whenever you may come* ... (time)
  Estés donde estés... *Wherever you may be* ... (place)
  Te vistas como te vistas... *However you may dress* ... (manner)
  Hagas lo que hagas... *Whatever you may do* ... (kind)
  Seas quien seas... *Whoever you may be* ... (identity)

- Although the translations sound quite formal, this type of construction is very common in everyday Spanish. In English, the equivalent would be more likely to be phrased as *whenever you come, wherever you are, no matter what you do*, etc.

---

10 Put the following words into the appropriate sentences:

→ *cuando / donde / como / lo que / quien*

a. Digas .... digas, no te creeré.

b. Vayas .... vayas, te seguiré.

c. Sea .... sea, esta tarde o esta noche, tengo que verte.

d. Llame .... llame, no estoy.

e. Bailes .... bailes, bien o mal, me gusta bailar contigo.

11 Complete the sentences with the appropriate conjugated form of these verbs:

→ *poner / llamar / venir / decir / conducir*

a. .... lo que .... mis amigos, lo haré.

b. .... quien .... a esta fiesta, yo no iré.

c. .... como ...., rápido o despacio, siempre tengo accidentes.

d. Las .... donde las ...., siempre pierdo las llaves.

e. .... cuando ...., aunque sea tarde, te contestaré.

Bravo! You've completed Lesson 15. It's time to count up the icons for the exercises and record your results here and in the table on page 128.

Compound tenses & auxiliary verbs

The active and passive voice

- The passive voice is formed by making the object of an active sentence the subject using **ser** *to be* (conjugated) + past participle. In Spanish, the passive voice is less common than in English. For example, a sentence such as *I was surprised by his words* would normally use the active voice: **Me han sorprendido sus palabras.** *His words surprised me.*

- As the past participle in the passive voice is used as an adjective, its ending needs to change to agree with the subject in gender and number. If you want to specify the agent (who or what performs the action), it can be introduced with **por** *by*.

> El escritor publica la novela.
> → **La novela es publicada por el escritor.**
> El músico ha compuesto la canción.
> → **La canción ha sido compuesta por el músico.**
> El arquitecto construyó estas casas.
> → **Estas casas fueron construidas por el arquitecto.**
> Los científicos realizarán nuevos inventos.
> → **Nuevos inventos serán realizados por los científicos.**

- Note that **ser** can be conjugated in all tenses and moods in the passive voice. See the box for some examples of sentences contrasting the active and passive voice.

Read the sentences and decide if they are in the active or the passive voice and tick the appropriate box.

	Active voice	Passive voice
a. La puerta fue abierta por el viento.	☐	☐
b. Mi primo me ha invitado para su cumpleaños.	☐	☐
c. Juan ha escrito estos cuadernos de ejercicios.	☐	☐
d. Estos cuadernos son utilizados por muchas personas.	☐	☐
e. El año que viene, otro cuaderno será publicado por Assimil.	☐	☐
f. Estos autores son muy apreciados por el público.	☐	☐
g. Las empresas contratan a las personas que saben idiomas.	☐	☐
h. Ojalá mis amigos no sean despedidos por la empresa.	☐	☐

2 Now rewrite the sentences from the preceding exercise, using the passive voice if they are in the active voice and vice versa.

a. ....

b. ....

c. ....

d. ....

e. ....

f. ....

g. ....

h. ....

A note on *para* and *por*

These two prepositions deserve a special mention as their usage can be tricky.

- **para** is used to indicate purpose, use, intention, effect or direction in the sense of *for* or *in order to*.
  Leo la prensa para seguir la actualidad. *I read the press in order to keep up with current events.*
  Este regalo es para ti. *This present is for you.*
  No estoy hecho para las matemáticas. *I'm not cut out for maths.*
  El cuchillo suizo sirve para todo. *The Swiss army knife is used for everything.*
  Para la semana que viene tengo que... *For/By next week I have to...*
  El autobús sale para Madrid a las tres. *The bus leaves for Madrid at 3:00.*

- **para** can also be used to give an opinion or point of view:
  Para mí, Messi es mejor que Ronaldo. *For me, Messi is better than Ronaldo.*

- **por** is used to indicate spatial concepts such as *by*, *through*, *around*:
  Siempre paso por Madrid. *I always go via Madrid.*
  Vive por el barrio de Salamanca. *He lives somewhere in the Salamanca neighbourhood.*

- **por** is also used in various time phrases:
  por la tarde *in the afternoon*
  tres veces por día *three times a day*

- **por** can also show cause, e.g. *for*, *because of*:
  Lo hago por amistad. *I do it out of friendship.*
  Lucha por sus ideas. *She fights for her ideas.*

3 Complete the following sentences with *por* or *para*.

a. .... llegar a casa, lo mejor es que pases .... aquí.

b. He reservado una mesa .... cuatro personas.

c. No me gusta trabajar .... la noche.

d. Viene a verme una vez .... año.

e. ¿............ dónde estará? Hace días que no lo veo.

f. ¿Estás cansado? Eso te pasa .... acostarte tan tarde.

g. .... su capacidad, es un coche .... familias numerosas.

h. ¿Me podrías entregar el trabajo .... el martes?

4 Translate the following sentences (the *you* is informal singular).

a. To eat a good paella, go to this restaurant.

....

....

b. I have brought something for you.

....

c. Sport is good for your ('the') health.

....

d. I travelled around Spain this summer.

....

e. In the morning I drink coffee.

....

f. In your opinion, which is the best film?

....

g. I want this work [done] by tomorrow.

....

The auxiliary verbs 'to have' and 'to be'

- Compound verbs are made up of more than one word. The Spanish perfect tenses are formed with a conjugated form of the auxiliary verb **haber** *to have* + past participle. (Don't confuse **tener** *to have*, in the sense of possession, and **haber**, which is mainly used as an auxiliary in compound verbs.)

  He comido. *I have eaten.*   **Ha hablado.** *He has spoken.*   **Han ido.** *They have gone.*

- The progressive tenses (to show an action happening right now) use a conjugated form of **estar** *to be* + present participle: **Pedro está comiendo.** *Pedro is eating.*

- However, when **estar** is used with a <u>past</u> participle, the latter functions as an adjective: **El vaso está roto.** (This is not a compound tense, just verb + adjective.)

- The passive voice is formed with **ser** + past participle (which must agree in gender and number with the subject): <u>Las revistas</u> son publicad<u>as</u> por el editor.

In these sentences, only one of the suggestions is correct. Cross out the others.

a. Juan [**se ha arruinado / se es arruinado / se está arruinado**] con el juego.

b. Soy español, [**he nacido / estoy nacido**] en Sevilla.

c. Como la puerta estaba cerrada, [**estoy entrado / soy entrado / he entrado**] por la ventana.

d. Juan [**ha insatisfecho / está insatisfecho**] con el resultado del partido.

e. Yo [**soy cerrado / estoy cerrado / he cerrado**] bien la puerta: ¿por qué [**es abierta / está abierta / ha abierta**]?

f. Como hacía buen tiempo, [**somos salidos / hemos salido / estamos salidos**] a pasear.

g. La empresa lo [**está despedido / ha despedido / es despedido**]: no tiene trabajo y [**está desesperado / ha desesperado / es desesperado**].

h. ¡Si mis gafas [**están rotas / son rotas**] es que alguien las [**está roto / es roto / ha roto**]!

6 Translate these sentences.

a. We've come up to see you *(sing. inf.)*.

....

b. They have returned to buy the bread.

....

c. The doors are completely ('well') closed.

....

d. The door was opened by the wind.

....

e. This film has been seen by lots of people.

....

....

f. I have broken my glasses.

....

g. My glasses are broken.

....

h. This book is well written.

....

Forming the perfect tenses

- The various perfect tenses are formed simply by conjugating the auxiliary verb **haber** in the appropriate tense + past participle, e.g.:

  Lo ha hecho. *He has done it.* (present perfect)
  Lo había hecho. *He had done it.* (past perfect)
  Lo habría hecho. *He would have done it.* (conditional perfect)
  No creo que lo haya hecho. *I don't believe he has done it.* (present perfect subj.)
  Si hubiera podido… *If he could have…* (past perfect subjunctive)

- Note that in the conditional perfect, the auxiliary **hubiera** is often used in place of **habría**:

  Si lo hubiera sabido, lo habría / hubiera dicho. *If I had known, I would have said so.*

		The auxiliary *haber*		
present	imperfect	conditional	present subj.	imperfect subj.
he	había	habría	haya	hubiera
has	habías	habría	hayas	hubieras
ha	había	habrías	haya	hubiera
hemos	habíamos	habríamos	hayamos	hubiéramos
habéis	habíais	habríais	hayáis	hubierais
han	habían	habrían	hayan	hubieran

7 Form five 'unreal' (contrary-to-fact) conditional sentences in the first-person singular (*If I were… I would be…*) from the appropriate pairs of phrases below.

abrir la puerta

mi móvil / tener cobertura

ser más alto

hacer un gran viaje por América latina

hacer mal tiempo

tener la llave

escribir un mensaje

jugar al baloncesto

ponerme la gabardina

saber hablar español

a. Si ....

b. Si ....

c. Si ....

d. Si ....

e. Si ....

8 Now rewrite the sentences from the previous exercise to form 'unreal' conditional sentences from a perspective in the past (*If I had been..., I would have been...*).

a. Si ....

b. Si ....

c. Si ....

d. Si ....

e. Si ....

9 Complete the perfect tenses in these sentences using the appropriate form of the auxiliary verb *haber*.

habia   haya   habría   hubiera   ha

a. Si no .... comprado este cuaderno, no .... repasado la gramática.

b. No .... hecho tantos ejercicios en mi vida.

c. Cuando .... repasado toda la gramática, hablaré bastante mejor español.

d. Siempre me .... encantado aprender idiomas.

Well done! You've reached the end of Lesson 16. It's time to count up the icons for the exercises and record your result here and in the table on page 128.

Vocabulary and comprehension 3: clothing

Shopping for clothes in Spain

- **El Corte Inglés** is still the most famous Spanish department store chain, with outlets in all of Spain's major cities. More recently, it has had competition in the clothing industry from large groups such as **Zara**, **Mango** and **Cortefiel**, which appeal to the younger market, especially with brands including **Bershka**, **Pull&Bear** and **Sfera**.

- In terms of footwear, **Camper** is a long-established company that today has a very trendy, 'green' image. For outdoor activities, **Coronel Tapiocca** is a complete outfitter for hiking enthusiasts.

- See the box for a brief list of useful words for various kinds of clothing.

la camisa *shirt*	
la camiseta *T-shirt*	
la cazadora *jacket (denim/leather)*	
el chándal *tracksuit*	
la chaqueta *jacket*	
las deportivas *trainers/tennis shoes*	
la falda *skirt*	
la gorra *cap*	
el pantalón *trousers*	
la ropa *clothes*	
los vaqueros *jeans*	
el vestido *dress*	
los zapatos *shoes*	

I Put these five pieces of text in order (from María Menéndez-Ponte's "No tengo nada que ponerme" *Maldita adolescente*, Editorial SM, 2001):

........./........./........./........./.........

A
– Pues no sé... Con un top, una mini...
– Vamos, de lo que tienes lleno el armario.

C
– ¡Pero mamá, qué cursilada! Nadie va así vestida a una fiesta.
– ¿Cómo van entonces?

B
– Pues es bien mona.
– Sí, será monísima, pero tú no conoces a mis amigas, van todas de marca.
– ¡Vaya bobada!

E
– ¿Lleno, dices? A ver, ¿cuántas minifaldas tengo?
– Que yo recuerde, tres.
– Si cuentas las dos que no me sirven... Y encima la que tengo es de Continente. ¿Cómo voy a ir a una fiesta con una falda de Continente?

D
– Oye, ¿y qué te vas a poner?
– No tengo nada.
– ¿Cómo que no tienes nada? ¿Y el vestido de las Navidades?

2 Based on the previous text, tick the correct end of each sentence.

a. Los dos personajes de este diálogo son…

☐ una madre y su hija. ☐ dos compañeras de colegio. ☐ dos hermanas.

b. La joven que habla va a ir…

☐ al colegio. ☐ a una actividad extraescolar. ☐ a una fiesta.

c. Según ella, sus amigas van a vestir…

☐ la ropa cotidiana. ☐ la ropa de Navidad. ☐ un top y una minifalda.

d. No quiere ponerse las faldas que tiene…

☐ porque no le gusta el color. ☐ porque no son de marca. ☐ porque son de marca.

3 In the context of this text, what do you think these words or expressions mean?

a. Una cursilada:

☐ something outdated
☐ something ridiculous
☐ something that's a bargain

b. ¡Vaya bobada!

☐ How silly!
☐ How stylish!
☐ How painful!

c. Pues no sé…:

☐ Well, it's not me …
☐ Well, don't go there …
☐ Well, I don't know …

d. Es bien mona:

☐ It's really cute.
☐ There's only one.
☐ Well, too bad.

4 Using words from the text, translate the following sentences.

a. Your *(informal)* skirt may come from Primark, but it's very cute.

→ ....

b. All my friends *(f.)* wear brand-name clothing.

→ ....

c. Your *(informal)* wardrobe is full of dresses and miniskirts.

→ ....

d. I don't want to go to a party dressed like that.

→ ....

e. How can you *(informal)* say you have nothing to wear?

→ ....

5 Can you give the Spanish word for each of these items of clothing, without referring back to p. 110?

a. ....

b. ....

c. ....

d. ....

e. ....

f. ....

g. ....

h. ....

i. ....

6 And finally, *un damero maldito*! As on p. 77, find the words that correspond to each definition and use the letters to fill in the grid, then write out and translate the hidden sentence.

a. Plato típico de España a base de arroz

10	27	38	7	17	1

b. La madre de mi mujer

2	35	18	23	12	22

c. Cuarenta y cinco entre tres

14	24	6	40	34	8

d. Demostrativo y también letra del alfabeto

16	9	30

e. Sentimiento que une a los amigos

20	5	4	31	26	13	37

f. El día tiene veinticuatro

19	41	39	36	3

g. Pronombre para el tratamiento formal

15	25	32	11	28

h. 3ª persona del singular del presente de oír

29	21	33

1	2	3	4	5	6	7
■	8	9	10	11	12	13
■	14	15	16	■	17	18
■	19	20	21	22	■	23
24	25	26	27	28	29	■
30	31	32	33	■	34	35
36	37	38	39	40	41	■

i. La frase escondida es:

....

....

....

....

j. Y su traducción es:

....

....

....

....

¡Felicidades! You've now completed all of the exercises in this workbook! It's time to count up the icons for this section and record your result here and in the final table on page 128.

Verb conjugation tables

Infinitivo *(infinitive)*	Presente de indicativo *(present indicative)*		Presente de subjuntivo *(present subjunctive)*		Imperativo *(imperative – informal)*		Pretérito imperfecto de indicativo *(imperfect indicative)*	
Regular verbs								
hablar *to talk /* *speak*	**hablo** **hablas** **habla**	**hablamos** **habláis** **hablan**	**hable** **hables** **hable**	**hablemos** **habléis** **hablen**	**habla**	**hablad**	**hablaba** **hablabas** **hablaba**	**hablábamos** **hablabais** **hablaban**
aprender *to learn*	**aprendo** **aprendes** **aprende**	**aprendemos** **aprendéis** **aprenden**	**aprenda** **aprendas** **aprenda**	**aprendamos** **aprendáis** **aprendan**	**aprende**	**aprended**	**aprendía** **aprendías** **aprendía**	**aprendíamos** **aprendíais** **aprendían**
vivir *to live*	**vivo** **vives** **vive**	**vivimos** **vivís** **viven**	**viva** **vivas** **viva**	**vivamos** **viváis** **vivan**	**vive**	**vivid**	**vivía** **vivías** **vivía**	**vivíamos** **vivíais** **vivían**
Stem-changing verbs: e ➜ ie & o ➜ ue								
pensar *to think*	**pienso** **piensas** **piensa**	**pensamos** **pensáis** **piensan**	**piense** **pienses** **piense**	**pensemos** **penséis** **piensen**	**piensa**	**pensad**	**pensaba** **pensabas** **pensaba**	**pensábamos** **pensabais** **pensaban**
entender *to under-* *stand*	**entiendo** **entiendes** **entiende**	**entendemos** **entendéis** **entienden**	**entienda** **entiendas** **entienda**	**entendamos** **entendáis** **entiendan**	**entiende**	**entended**	**entendía** **entendías** **entendía**	**entendíamos** **entendíais** **entendían**
contar *to tell,* *to count*	**cuento** **cuentas** **cuenta**	**contamos** **contáis** **cuentan**	**cuente** **cuentes** **cuente**	**contemos** **contéis** **cuenten**	**cuenta**	**contad**	**contaba** **contabas** **contaba**	**contábamos** **contabais** **contaban**
mover *to move*	**muevo** **mueves** **mueve**	**movemos** **movéis** **mueven**	**mueva** **muevas** **mueva**	**movamos** **mováis** **muevan**	**mueve**	**moved**	**movía** **movías** **movía**	**movíamos** **movíais** **movían**
Stem-changing verbs: e ➜ i								
pedir *to ask for /* *request*	**pido** **pides** **pide**	**pedimos** **pedís** **piden**	**pida** **pidas** **pida**	**pidamos** **pidáis** **pidan**	**pide**	**pedid**	**pedía** **pedías** **pedía**	**pedíamos** **pedíais** **pedían**

Verbs that take this stem change include: **corregir**, **despedir**, **elegir**, **impedir**, **medir**, **seguir**, **servir**, **vestir**.

Pretérito indefinido (preterite)		Pretérito imperfecto de subjuntivo (imperfect subjunctive)		Futuro (future)		Condicional (conditional)		Gerundio / Part. pasivo (present / past participle)	
hablé	hablamos	hablara	habláramos	hablaré	hablaremos	hablaría	hablaríamos	g.	hablando
hablaste	hablasteis	hablaras	hablarais	hablarás	hablaréis	hablarías	hablaríais	p.p.	hablado
habló	hablaron	hablara	hablaran	hablará	hablarán	hablaría	hablarían		
aprendí	aprendimos	aprendiera	aprendiéramos	aprenderé	aprenderemos	aprendería	aprenderíamos	g.	aprendiendo
aprendiste	aprendisteis	aprendieras	aprendierais	aprenderás	aprenderéis	aprenderías	aprenderíais	p.p.	aprendido
aprendió	aprendieron	aprendiera	aprendieran	aprenderá	aprenderán	aprendería	aprenderían		
viví	vivimos	viviera	viviéramos	viviré	viviremos	viviría	viviríamos	g.	viviendo
viviste	vivisteis	vivieras	vivierais	vivirás	viviréis	vivirías	viviríais	p.p.	vivido
vivió	vivieron	viviera	vivieran	vivirá	vivirán	viviría	vivirían		
pensé	pensamos	pensara	pensáramos	pensaré	pensaremos	pensaría	pensaríamos	g.	pensando
pensaste	pensasteis	pensaras	pensarais	pensarás	pensaréis	pensarías	pensaríais	p.p.	pensado
pensó	pensaron	pensara	pensaran	pensará	pensarán	pensaría	pensarían		
entendí	entendimos	entendiera	entendiéramos	entenderé	entenderemos	entendería	entenderíamos	g.	entendiendo
entendiste	entendisteis	entendieras	entendierais	entenderás	entenderéis	entenderías	entenderíais	p.p.	entendido
entendió	entendieron	entendiera	entendieran	entenderá	entenderán	entendería	entenderían		
conté	contamos	contara	contáramos	contaré	contaremos	contaría	contaríamos	g.	contando
contaste	contasteis	contaras	contarais	contarás	contaréis	contarías	contaríais	p.p.	contado
contó	contaron	contara	contaran	contará	contarán	contaría	contarían		
moví	movimos	moviera	moviéramos	moveré	moveremos	movería	moveríamos	g.	moviendo
moviste	movisteis	movieras	movierais	moverás	moveréis	moverías	moveríais	p.p.	movido
movió	movieron	moviera	movieran	moverá	moverán	movería	moverían		
pedí	pedimos	pidiera	pidiéramos	pediré	pediremos	pediría	pediríamos	g.	pidiendo
pediste	pedisteis	pidieras	pidierais	pedirás	pediréis	pedirías	pediríais	p.p.	pedido
pidió	pidieron	pidiera	pidieran	pedirá	pedirán	pediría	pedirían		

Infinitivo (infinitive)	Presente de indicativo (present indicative)		Presente de subjuntivo (present subjunctive)		Imperativo (imperative – informal)		Pretérito imperfecto de indicativo (imperfect indicative)	
Stem-changing verbs: e ➜ ie / i & o ➜ ue / u								
sentir to feel, to regret	siento sientes siente	sentimos sentís sienten	sienta sientas sienta	sintamos sintáis sientan	siente	sentid	sentía sentías sentía	sentíamos sentíais sentían
Verbs that take this stem change include: divertir, mentir, preferir, sugerir.								
dormir to sleep	duermo duermes duerme	dormimos dormís duermen	duerma duermas duerma	durmamos durmáis duerman	duerme	dormid	dormía dormías dormía	dormíamos dormíais dormían
Verbs that take this stem change include: **morir.**								
Most verbs ending in -cer or -cir (e.g. conocer): c ➜ zc								
conocer to know, to meet	conozco conoces conoce	conocemos conocéis conocen	conozca conozcas conozca	conozcamos conozcáis conozcan	conoce	conoced	conocía conocías conocía	conocíamos conocíais conocían
Verbs that take this stem change include: **nacer, obedecer, padecer, parecer, pertenecer, relucir.**								
Verbs ending in -ducir (e.g. conducir): c ➜ zc (➜ j in the preterite, imperfect subjunctive & future subjunctive)								
conducir to drive	conduzco conduces conduce	conducimos conducís conducen	conduzca conduzcas conduzca	conduzcamos conduzcáis conduzcan	conduce	conducid	conducía conducías conducía	conducíamos conducíais conducían
Verbs that take this stem change include: **deducir, introducir, producir, seducir, traducir.**								

Pretérito indefinido (preterite)		Pretérito imperfecto de subjuntivo (imperfect subjunctive)		Futuro (future)		Condicional (conditional)		Gerundio / Part. pasivo (present / past participle)	
sentí	sentimos	sintiera	sintiéramos	sentiré	sentiremos	sentiría	sentiríamos	g.	sintiendo
sentiste	sentisteis	sintieras	sintierais	sentirás	sentiréis	sentirías	sentiríais	p.p.	sentido
sintió	sintieron	sintiera	sintieran	sentirá	sentirán	sentiría	sentirían		
dormí	dormimos	durmiera	durmiéramos	dormiré	dormiremos	dormiría	dormiríamos	g.	durmiendo
dormiste	dormisteis	durmieras	durmierais	dormirás	dormiréis	dormirías	dormiríais	p.p.	dormido
durmió	durmieron	durmiera	durmieran	dormirá	dormirán	dormiría	dormirían		
conocí	conocimos	conociera	conociéramos	conoceré	conoceremos	conocería	conoceríamos	g.	conociendo
conociste	conocisteis	conocieras	conocierais	conocerás	conoceréis	conocerías	conoceríais	p.p.	conocido
conoció	conocieron	conociera	conocieran	conocerá	conocerán	conocería	conocerían		
conduje	condujimos	condujera	condujéramos	conduciré	conduciremos	conduciría	conduciríamos	g.	conduciendo
condujiste	condujisteis	condujeras	condujerais	conducirás	conduciréis	conducirías	conduciríais	p.p.	conducido
condujo	condujeron	condujera	condujeran	conducirá	conducirán	conduciría	conducirían		

Infinitivo (infinitive)	Presente de indicativo (present indicative)		Presente de subjuntivo (present subjunctive)		Imperativo (imperative – informal)		Pretérito imperfecto de indicativo (imperfect indicative)	
Some uniquely irregular verbs								
andar to walk	ando andas anda	andamos andáis andan	ande andes ande	andemos andéis anden	anda	andad	andaba andabas andaba	andábamos andabais andaban
caber to fit (into)	quepo cabes cabe	cabemos cabéis caben	quepa quepas quepa	quepamos quepáis quepan	cabe	cabed	cabía cabías cabía	cabíamos cabíais cabían
caer to fall	caigo caes cae	caemos caéis caen	caiga caigas caiga	caigamos caigáis caigan	cae	caed	caía caías caía	caíamos caíais caían
dar to give	doy das da	damos dais dan	dé des dé	demos deis den	da	dad	daba dabas daba	dábamos dabais daban
decir to say / tell	digo dices dice	decimos decís dicen	diga digas diga	digamos digáis digan	di	decid	decía decías decía	decíamos decíais decían
estar to be	estoy estás está	estamos estáis están	esté estés esté	estemos estéis estén	está	estad	estaba estabas estaba	estábamos estabais estaban
haber to have (auxiliary verb)	he has ha	hemos habéis han	haya hayas haya	hayamos hayáis hayan	–	–	había habías había	habíamos habíais habían
hacer to do, to make	hago haces hace	hacemos hacéis hacen	haga hagas haga	hagamos hagáis hagan	haz	haced	hacía hacías hacía	hacíamos hacíais hacían
ir to go	voy vas va	vamos vais van	vaya vayas vaya	vayamos vayáis vayan	ve	id	iba ibas iba	íbamos ibais iban
oír to hear	oigo oyes oye	oímos oís oyen	oiga oigas oiga	oigamos oigáis oigan	oye	oíd	oía oías oía	oíamos oíais oían
poder to be able to (can)	puedo puedes puede	podemos podéis pueden	pueda puedas pueda	podamos podáis puedan	–	–	podía podías podía	podíamos podíais podían

Pretérito indefinido (preterite)		Pretérito imperfecto de subjuntivo (imperfect subjunctive)		Futuro (future)		Condicional (conditional)		Gerundio / Part. pasivo (present / past participle)	
anduve	anduvimos	anduviera	anduviéramos	andaré	andaremos	andaría	andaríamos	g.	andando
anduviste	anduvisteis	anduvieras	anduvierais	andarás	andaréis	andarías	andaríais	p.p.	andado
anduvo	anduvieron	anduviera	anduvieran	andará	andarán	andaría	andarían		
cupe	cupimos	cupiera	cupiéramos	cabré	cabremos	cabría	cabríamos	g.	cabiendo
cupiste	cupisteis	cupieras	cupierais	cabrás	cabréis	cabrías	cabríais	p.p.	cabido
cupo	cupieron	cupiera	cupieran	cabrá	cabrán	cabría	cabrían		
caí	caímos	cayera	cayéramos	caeré	caeremos	caería	caeríamos	g.	cayendo
caíste	caísteis	cayeras	cayerais	caerás	caeréis	caerías	caeríais	p.p.	caído
cayó	cayeron	cayera	cayeran	caerá	caerán	caería	caerían		
di	dimos	diera	diéramos	daré	daremos	daría	daríamos	g.	dando
diste	disteis	dieras	dierais	darás	daréis	darías	daríais	p.p.	dado
dio	dieron	diera	dieran	dará	darán	daría	darían		
dije	dijimos	dijera	dijéramos	diré	diremos	diría	diríamos	g.	diciendo
dijiste	dijisteis	dijeras	dijerais	dirás	diréis	dirías	diríais	p.p.	dicho
dijo	dijeron	dijera	dijeran	dirá	dirán	diría	dirían		
estuve	estuvimos	estuviera	estuviéramos	estaré	estaremos	estaría	estaríamos	g.	estando
estuviste	estuvisteis	estuvieras	estuvierais	estarás	estaréis	estarías	estaríais	p.p.	estado
estuvo	estuvieron	estuviera	estuvieran	estará	estarán	estaría	estarían		
hube	hubimos	hubiera	hubiéramos	habré	habremos	habría	habríamos	g.	habiendo
hubiste	hubisteis	hubieras	hubierais	habrás	habréis	habrías	habríais	p.p.	habido
hubo	hubieron	hubiera	hubieran	habrá	habrán	habría	habrían		
hice	hicimos	hiciera	hiciéramos	haré	haremos	haría	haríamos	g.	haciendo
hiciste	hicisteis	hicieras	hicierais	harás	haréis	harías	haríais	p.p.	hecho
hizo	hicieron	hiciera	hicieran	hará	harán	haría	harían		
fui	fuimos	fuera	fuéramos	iré	iremos	iría	iríamos	g.	yendo
fuiste	fuisteis	fueras	fuerais	irás	iréis	irías	iríais	p.p.	ido
fue	fueron	fuera	fueran	irá	irán	iría	irían		
oí	oímos	oyera	oyéramos	oiré	oiremos	oiría	oiríamos	g.	oyendo
oíste	oísteis	oyeras	oyerais	oirás	oiréis	oirías	oiríais	p.p.	oído
oyó	oyeron	oyera	oyeran	oirá	oirán	oiría	oirían		
pude	pudimos	pudiera	pudiéramos	podré	podremos	podría	podríamos	g.	pudiendo
pudiste	pudisteis	pudieras	pudierais	podrás	podréis	podrías	podríais	p.p.	podido
pudo	pudieron	pudiera	pudieran	podrá	podrán	podría	podrían		

Infinitivo (infinitive)	Presente de indicativo (present indicative)		Presente de subjuntivo (present subjunctive)		Imperativo (imperative – informal)		Pretérito imperfecto de indicativo (imperfect indicative)	
Some uniquely irregular verbs								
poner *to put*	pongo pones pone	ponemos ponéis ponen	ponga pongas ponga	pongamos pongáis pongan	pon	poned	ponía ponías ponía	poníamos poníais ponían
querer *to want, to love*	quiero quieres quiere	queremos queréis quieren	quiera quieras quiera	queramos queráis quieran	quiere	quered	quería querías quería	queríamos queríais querían
saber *to know*	sé sabes sabe	sabemos sabéis saben	sepa sepas sepa	sepamos sepáis sepan	sabe	sabed	sabía sabías sabía	sabíamos sabíais sabían
salir *to leave, to go out*	salgo sales sale	salimos salís salen	salga salgas salga	salgamos salgáis salgan	sal	salid	salía salías salía	salíamos salíais salían
ser *to be*	soy eres es	somos sois son	sea seas sea	seamos seáis sean	sé	sed	era eras era	éramos erais eran
tener *to have, to possess*	tengo tienes tiene	tenemos tenéis tienen	tenga tengas tenga	tengamos tengáis tengan	ten	tened	tenía tenías tenía	teníamos teníais tenían
traer *to bring*	traigo traes trae	traemos traéis traen	traiga traigas traiga	traigamos traigáis traigan	trae	traed	traía traías traía	traíamos traíais traían
valer *to be worth*	valgo vales vale	valemos valéis valen	valga valgas valga	valgamos valgáis valgan	vale	valed	valía valías valía	valíamos valíais valían
venir *to come*	vengo vienes viene	venimos venís vienen	venga vengas venga	vengamos vengáis vengan	ven	venid	venía venías venía	veníamos veníais venían
ver *to see*	veo ves ve	vemos veis ven	vea veas vea	veamos veáis vean	ve	ved	veía veías veía	veíamos veíais veían

Pretérito indefinido (preterite)		Pretérito imperfecto de subjuntivo (imperfect subjunctive)		Futuro (future)		Condicional (conditional)		Gerundio / Part. pasivo (present / past participle)	
puse	pusimos	pusiera	pusiéramos	pondré	pondremos	pondría	pondríamos	g.	poniendo
pusiste	pusisteis	pusieras	pusierais	pondrás	pondréis	pondrías	pondríais	p.p.	puesto
puso	pusieron	pusiera	pusieran	pondrá	pondrán	pondría	pondrían		
quise	quisimos	quisiera	quisiéramos	querré	querremos	querría	querríamos	g.	queriendo
quisiste	quisisteis	quisieras	quisierais	querrás	querréis	querrías	querríais	p.p.	querido
quiso	quisieron	quisiera	quisieran	querrá	querrán	querría	querrían		
supe	supimos	supiera	supiéramos	sabré	sabremos	sabría	sabríamos	g.	sabiendo
supiste	supisteis	supieras	supierais	sabrás	sabréis	sabrías	sabríais	p.p.	sabido
supo	supieron	supiera	supieran	sabrá	sabrán	sabría	sabrían		
salí	salimos	saliera	saliéramos	saldré	saldremos	saldría	saldríamos	g.	saliendo
saliste	salisteis	salieras	salierais	saldrás	saldréis	saldrías	saldríais	p.p.	salido
salió	salieron	saliera	salieran	saldrá	saldrán	saldría	saldrían		
fui	fuimos	fuera	fuéramos	seré	seremos	sería	seríamos	g.	siendo
fuiste	fuisteis	fueras	fuerais	serás	seréis	serías	seríais	p.p.	sido
fue	fueron	fuera	fueran	será	serán	sería	serían		
tuve	tuvimos	tuviera	tuviéramos	tendré	tendremos	tendría	tendríamos	g.	teniendo
tuviste	tuvisteis	tuvieras	tuvierais	tendrás	tendréis	tendrías	tendríais	p.p.	tenido
tuvo	tuvieron	tuviera	tuvieran	tendrá	tendrán	tendría	tendrían		
traje	trajimos	trajera	trajéramos	traeré	traeremos	traería	traeríamos	g.	trayendo
trajiste	trajisteis	trajeras	trajerais	traerás	traeréis	traerías	traeríais	p.p.	traído
trajo	trajeron	trajera	trajeran	traerá	traerán	traería	traerían		
valí	valimos	valiera	valiéramos	valdré	valdremos	valdría	valdríamos	g.	valiendo
valiste	valisteis	valieras	valierais	valdrás	valdréis	valdrías	valdríais	p.p.	valido
valió	valieron	valiera	valieran	valdrá	valdrán	valdría	valdrían		
vine	vinimos	viniera	viniéramos	vendré	vendremos	vendría	vendríamos	g.	viniendo
viniste	vinisteis	vinieras	vinierais	vendrás	vendréis	vendrías	vendríais	p.p.	venido
vino	vinieron	viniera	vinieran	vendrá	vendrán	vendría	vendrían		
vi	vimos	viera	viéramos	veré	veremos	vería	veríamos	g.	viendo
viste	visteis	vieras	vierais	verás	veréis	verías	veríais	p.p.	visto
vio	vieron	viera	vieran	verá	verán	vería	verían		

1. Letters, sounds & punctuation

① **a. DVD** *(DE UVE DE)* **b. GPS** *(GE PE ESE)* **c. DNI** *(DE ENE I)* **d. WWW** *(UVE DOBLE UVE DOBLE UVE DOBLE)* **e. ONG** *(O ENE GE)* **f. HTTP** *(HACHE TE TE PE)*.

② **a. Silent:** hasta, hay, helado, hija, hola, huevo **b. Like [th] in English:** zorro, cero, zapato, ciruela, zoológico, zumo **c. Like the Spanish jota:** julio, jamón, gitano, girasol, jirafa, gel **d. Like a hard [g] in English:** guitarra, guerra, gorra, gafas, gato, golondrina **e. Like [k] in English:** queso, cumpleaños, calor, quizás, camino, colega.

③

a. Francia					✔
b. México	✔				
c. España		✔			
d. Portugal			✔		
e. Perú				✔	
f. Bélgica	✔				
g. Canadá			✔		
h. Holanda		✔			
i. Suiza					✔
j. Brasil				✔	

④ **a.** paella ⬛⬛⬜ **b.** gambas ⬛⬜ **c.** arroz ⬜⬛ **d.** cerveza ⬜⬛⬜ **e.** mujer ⬜⬛ **f.** salud ⬜⬛ **g.** voleibol ⬜⬜⬛ **h.** Esteban ⬜⬛⬜ **i.** estadio ⬜⬛⬜ **j.** pasaporte ⬜⬜⬛⬜ **k.** Valladolid ⬜⬜⬜⬛ **l.** martes ⬛⬜.

⑤ **a.** francés **b.** Cádiz **c.** fútbol **d.** café **e.** París **f.** dólar **g.** menú **h.** sofá **i.** sándwich **j.** módem **k.** váter **l.** jamón.

⑥ **a.** dos árboles **b.** dos ingleses **c.** dos balones **d.** dos andenes **e.** dos móviles.

⑦ **a.** un alemán **b.** un portátil **c.** un papel **d.** un danés **e.** un mitin.

⑧ **a.** ¡Encantado! **b.** ¿Hablas español? **c.** ¡Bienvenido! **d.** ¿De dónde eres? **e.** ¡Hola! **f.** ¿Cómo te llamas?

⑨ **a.** hache te te pe dos puntos barra doble uve doble uve doble uve doble punto assimil punto com **b.** belén guión bajo ausejo arroba hotmail punto com **c.** juan guión cordoba arroba gemail punto com.

2. Articles, nouns, adjectives & numbers

① **a.** Mujeres al borde de un ataque de nervios **b.** La cabaña del tío Tom **c.** El señor de los anillos **d.** La guerra de las galaxias **e.** Blancanieves y los siete enanitos **f.** El libro de la selva.

② **a.** El precio de la tortilla. **b.** Quiero tortilla. **c.** Quiero una tortilla. **d.** Quiero manzanas. **e.** El precio de los huevos. **f.** Quiero huevos. **g.** Quiero vino. **h.** Quiero un pan.

③ **a.** El producto del mercado **b.** La imagen de la ciudad **c.** La ley del país.

④ **Feminine singular:** la estudiante seria / la directora alegre / la tenista triste / la chica simpática / la pianista famosa / la escritora interesante / la amiga fiel / la cantante actual. **Masculine singular:** el estudiante serio / el director alegre / el tenista triste / el chico simpático / el pianista famoso / el escritor interesante / el amigo fiel / el cantante actual. **Feminine plural:** las estudiantes serias / las directoras alegres / las tenistas tristes / las chicas simpáticas / las pianistas famosas / las escritoras interesantes / las amigas fieles / las cantantes actuales. **Masculine plural:** los estudiantes serios / los directores alegres / los tenistas tristes / los chicos simpáticos / los pianistas famosos / los escritores interesantes / los amigos fieles / los cantantes actuales.

⑤ **a.** La sangre es roja. **b.** Los troncos de los árboles son marrones. **c.** La leche es blanca. **d.** Tus ojos son azules como el cielo. **e.** La hierba es verde. **f.** Las panteras son negras. **g.** El jamón de York es rosa. **h.** Los limones son amarillos.

⑥ **a.** Barack es estadounidense. Es de Nueva York. **b.** Jacques es belga. Es de Bruselas. **c.** Samia es marroquí. Es de Rabat. **d.** Fernanda es portuguesa. Es de Lisboa. **e.** Inge es alemana. Es de Berlín. **f.** Guadalupe es mexicana. Es de Cancún.

⑦ **a.** siete por once igual setenta y siete **b.** treinta y tres menos ocho igual veinticinco **c.** catorce más quince igual veintinueve **d.** ochenta y cuatro entre cuatro igual veintiuno.

⑧ **a.** cincuenta y siete **b.** ochenta y seis **c.** cuarenta y uno **d.** quince **e.** novecientos uno **f.** setecientos ocho **g.** dos **h.** cuatrocientos veintiuno **i.** tres mil trescientos treinta **j.** ciento sesenta y cuatro **k.** quinientos doce **l.** ciento noventa y nueve **m.** siete mil doscientos siete.

⑨ **a.** Trescientas cuarenta y siete manzanas **b.** Dos mil quinientas trece amigas **c.** Mil novecientas veintiocho tortillas.

3. Conjugation & personal pronouns

① **a.** You read: Leéis **b.** We sing: Cantamos **c.** He writes: Escribe **d.** I speak: Hablo **e.** I open: Abro **f.** We dance: Bailamos **g.** They read: Leen **h.** You eat: Comes **i.** You drink: Bebéis **j.** We live: Vivimos

② **a.** bailo: I dance **b.** vive: he/she lives **c.** escribís: you write **d.** abres: you open **e.** bebemos: we drink **f.** cantan: they sing **g.** hablamos: we speak **h.** comen: they eat **i.** habla: he/she speaks **j.** lee: he/she reads

③ **a.** Los leo. **b.** Lo compro. **c.** Los como. **d.** La toco. **e.** Las quiero. **f.** Las canto. **g.** La escribo. **h.** Lo hablo.

④ **a.** Nos escribe cartas. **b.** Nos las escribe. **c.** Os escribimos un mail. **d.** Os lo escribimos. **e.** Me lees libros. **f.** Me los lees. **g.** Te abren los brazos. **h.** Te los abren. **i.** Les abrimos la puerta. **j.** Se la abrimos. **k.** Le leo poesías. **l.** Se las leo.

⑤ **a.** El libro es para ellas. **b.** Cantas conmigo. **c.** Bailamos delante de ellos. **d.** Coméis después de nosotros. **e.** Visito a mis amigos. **f.** Como sin ti. **g.** Quiere comer contigo.

⑥ **a.** Me lavo las manos antes de comer. **b.** Me lavo los dientes después de comer. **c.** Como delante de la tele. **d.** Echo la siesta después de comer. **e.** Se esconde detrás de un árbol.

⑦ **a.** A ellos no les gustan los ordenadores. **b.** A nosotras nos gustan las gambas. **c.** A mí me gustan los ordenadores. **d.** A ti te encantan las gambas. **e.** A vosotros os gusta España. **f.** A él no le gusta leer libros.

⑧ **a.** ¿Cómo se llama usted? **b.** ¿Dónde vive usted? **c.** ¿Le gusta la paella? **d.** ¡No le comprendo! **e.** ¿Habla usted español? **f.** ¿Es usted inglesa? **g.** Quiero hablar con usted.

4. Possessives, demonstratives & indefinite pronouns

① **a.** Son mis cartas. **b.** Es nuestro pasaporte. **c.** Son vuestras guitarras. **d.** Son sus móviles. **e.** Son sus colegas. **f.** Es vuestro libro. **g.** Es tu perro. **h.** Son tus profesores. **i.** Son nuestras guitarras. **j.** Es su portátil. **k.** Es mi amigo. **l.** Es su balón.

② **a.** No es mi libro, es el tuyo. **b.** No son mis gafas, son las tuyas. **c.** No son mis amigos, son los tuyos. **d.** No es tu carta, es la mía. **e.** No es tu abuela, es la suya. **f.** No son mis primas, son las suyas. **g.** No es tu padre, es el suyo. **h.** No es su ordenador, es el mío. **i.** No son tus discos, son los míos.

③ **a.** La perra no es nuestra. **b.** El portátil es mío. **c.** Los libros son suyos / son de ellos. **d.** La guitarra no es tuya. **e.** Las manzanas no son vuestras. **f.** Los discos no son tuyos.

④ **Hablo con un colega:** tratamiento de tú **a.** ¿Es tu/tuya la cerveza? **b.** ¿Son tus/tuyas las gambas? **c.** ¿Son tus/tuyos los discos? **d.** ¿Es tu/tuyo el móvil? **Hablo con mis hermanos:** tratamiento de tú **e.** ¿Es vuestro/vuestro el libro? **f.** ¿Es vuestra/vuestra la consola? **g.** ¿Son vuestros/vuestros los patines? **h.** ¿Son vuestras/vuestras las camisetas? **Hablo con la abuela de un amigo:** tratamiento de usted **i.** ¿Es su/suyo el té? **j.** ¿Es su/suya la revista? **k.** ¿Son sus/suyos los zapatos? **l.** ¿Son sus/suyas las gafas?

⑤ a. No comprendo <u>nada</u>. *I don't understand anything.* **b.** Aquí <u>nadie</u> canta. *Here, no one is singing.* **c.** No quiero <u>nada</u>. *I don't want anything.* **d.** <u>Nadie</u> me comprende. *No one understands me.* **e.** No comprendo a <u>nadie</u>. *I don't understand anyone.* **f.** No es <u>nada</u> simpático. *He is not nice at all.* **g.** Aquí no vive <u>nadie</u>. *No one lives here.* **h.** <u>Nadie</u> me quiere. *Nobody loves me.*

⑥ a. ¿Comprendes <u>algo</u>? *Do you understand anything?* **b.** ¿A <u>alguien</u> no le gusta la paella? *Does anyone not like paella?* **c.** ¿Quieres beber <u>algo</u>? *Do you want something to drink?* **d.** ¿Quieres <u>algo</u>? *Do you want something?* **e.** Quiero hablar con <u>alguien</u>. *I want to speak to someone.* **f.** ¡<u>Alguien</u> te llama por teléfono! *Someone is calling you on the phone!* **g.** ¿Vive <u>alguien</u> aquí? *Does anyone live here?* **h.** Hablo <u>algo</u> de inglés. *I speak a bit of English.*

⑦ a. Me gusta bañarme <u>aquí</u>, en esta playa. **b.** Aquella playa, <u>allí</u>, es muy peligrosa. **c.** ¿Qué es eso que llevas <u>ahí</u>? **d.** ¿Comemos <u>aquí</u>, en este restaurante? **e.** ¿Qué es aquello que veo <u>allí</u>? **f.** Escribe tu número <u>ahí</u>, en esa libreta.

⑧ a. *I like taking a swim here, on this beach.* **b.** *That beach over there is very dangerous.* **c.** *What is that you're carrying there?* **d.** *Shall we eat here, in this restaurant?* **e.** *What's that that I see over there?* **f.** *Write your number here, on this notepad.*

⑨ a. ¿Es tuyo <u>ese</u> bolígrafo, ahí en tu mesa? **b.** Quiero <u>estas</u> manzanas, aquí, las rojas. **c.** En <u>aquellos</u> tiempos, no existían los ordenadores. **d.** Yo vivo aquí, en <u>esta</u> casa azul. **e.** Mi abuelo vive allí, en <u>aquella</u> casa verde. **f.** ¿Son vuestros <u>esos</u> zapatos, ahí en el suelo?

5. *Ser, estar* & the progressive tenses

❶ a. <u>Soy</u> española. **b.** <u>Eres</u> médico. **c.** <u>Es</u> alta. **d.** <u>Son</u> simpáticos. **e.** <u>Estáis</u> cansados. **f.** <u>Estáis</u> indignadas. **g.** <u>Estamos</u> contentas. **h.** <u>Son</u> creyentes. **i.** <u>Estás</u> enfermo.

❷ a. Las aceitunas <u>son</u> buenas para la salud. **b.** Estas aceitunas <u>están</u> muy buenas. **c.** Este perro <u>es</u> muy vivo. **d.** ¡El perro <u>está</u> vivo! **e.** Mi padre <u>es</u> muy joven. **f.** Mi padre <u>está</u> muy joven. **g.** Mis hermanas <u>son</u> morenas. **h.** Mis hermanas <u>están</u> morenas. **i.** ¡Qué guapa <u>eres</u>! **j.** ¡Qué guapa <u>estás</u>!

❸ a. La solución no <u>es</u> evidente. **b.** Nosotros <u>estamos</u> en París. **c.** El problema no <u>está</u> ahí. **d.** ¿Qué día <u>es</u> hoy? **e.** Yo <u>soy</u> inglés, <u>soy</u> de Londres. **f.** <u>Es</u> la una de la tarde. **g.** La fiesta nacional <u>es</u> el 12 de octubre. **h.** ¿Qué hora <u>es</u>? **i.** La solución <u>está</u> en el trabajo. **j.** Mi cumpleaños <u>es</u> en primavera. **k.** No te veo: ¿dónde <u>estás</u>? **l.** Perdón, ¿qué día <u>es</u>/<u>estamos</u> hoy? **m.** El problema <u>es</u> importante. **n.** El interés de la película <u>está</u> en los personajes. **o.** Pedro no <u>está</u> en casa. **p.** <u>Es</u> la una de la mañana. **q.** Nochebuena <u>es</u> la noche del 24 de diciembre.

❹ a. Estoy abriendo la puerta. **b.** ¿A quién estáis llamando? **c.** Estamos comprando el pan.

❺ Present participle: bailando – bebiendo – tocando – hablando – comiendo – viviendo.
Infinitive: bailar – beber – tocar – hablar – comer – vivir.

❻ a. Pedro y Juan <u>están comiendo</u> una buena paella. **b.** Yo <u>estoy bebiendo</u> vino y tú <u>estás bebiendo</u> cerveza. **c.** Mi hermano <u>está tocando</u> la guitarra con sus amigos. **d.** Este año nosotros <u>estamos viviendo</u> en Londres. **e.** Lo que vosotros <u>estáis bailando</u> no es reggaetón, es cumbia. **f.** ¿De qué me <u>estás hablando</u>? ¡No te entiendo!

❼ a. ¡<u>Soy</u> yo! **b.** ¡<u>Somos</u> nosotros! **c.** ¡<u>Son</u> ellos! **d.** ¡<u>Es</u> usted!

❽ a. Este anillo no <u>es</u> de oro. **b.** ¿De quién <u>es</u> este anillo? **c.** Tú <u>estás</u> de buen humor. **d.** ¿Usted <u>es</u> de Madrid? **e.** ¿Usted <u>es</u> de aquí? **f.** No, nosotros no <u>somos</u> de aquí. **g.** Nosotros <u>estamos</u> de viaje por España. **h.** Yo <u>estoy</u> de fiesta con unos amigos.

❾ Hola, ¿<u>está</u> Carmen? / Sí, <u>soy</u> yo. / ¡Carmen! <u>Soy</u> Juan, ¿cómo <u>estás</u>? / ¡Juan! ¡Qué contenta <u>estoy</u> de hablar contigo! ¿Dónde <u>estás</u>? / <u>Estamos</u> de fin de semana en Londres Isabel y yo.

6. Present tense irregularities & simple sentences

❶ a. Los niños <u>mienten</u> frecuentemente a sus padres. **b.** Yo <u>me divierto</u> mucho con la consola. **c.** Cuando <u>vuelvo</u> del trabajo, estoy muy cansado. **d.** Cuando estamos lejos, no <u>nos acordamos</u> de las personas. **e.** ¿Tú <u>entiendes</u> lo que te estoy explicando? **f.** Te quiero mucho y <u>pienso</u> mucho en ti. **g.** ¿Vosotros <u>cerráis</u> la puerta con llave cuando salís? **h.** La clase comienza cuando los alumnos <u>se sientan</u>. **i.** Los abuelos siempre <u>cuentan</u> historias a sus nietos. **j.** Nosotros <u>perdemos</u> mucho tiempo jugando con la Play Station. **k.** Mi hijo de dos años es muy listo: ¡<u>cuenta</u> hasta diez! **l.** ¿Vosotros <u>dormís</u> la siesta por las tardes?

❷ a. No, no conozco Barcelona. **b.** No, no oigo nada. **c.** No, no salgo a pasear. **d.** No, no me pongo la gabardina. **e.** No, no conduzco bien. **f.** No, no tengo nada. **g.** No, no digo nada. **h.** No, no tengo dinero. **i.** No, no vengo contigo. **j.** No, no traduzco del inglés. **k.** No, no te reconozco. **l.** No, no te obedezco.

❸ a. ¿Cómo estás? **b.** ¿Cuánto cuesta? **c.** ¿Cuál es tu coche? **d.** ¿Cuándo es tu cumpleaños? **e.** ¿Cuáles son tus zapatos? **f.** ¿Quiénes son los padres de este niño? **g.** ¿Cuánta leche quiere? **h.** ¿Qué quieres? **i.** ¿Cuántos hermanos tienes? **j.** ¿Cuántas hermanas tienes? **k.** ¿Dónde vives? **l.** ¿Quién es el siguiente?

❹ a. ¡<u>Cuánto</u> habla mi suegra! **b.** ¡<u>Qué</u> difíciles son estos problemas! **c.** ¡<u>Cuántas</u> amigas tienes en facebook! **d.** ¡<u>Qué</u> alta es esta chica! **e.** ¡<u>Cuánto</u> duermen los bebés! **f.** ¡<u>Cuántos</u> perros hay en esta casa! **g.** ¡<u>Qué</u> tarde venís! **h.** ¡<u>Cuánto</u> dinero tiene este hombre!

❺ a. ¡Qué libro más (tan) interesante! **b.** ¡Qué perra más (tan) simpática! **c.** ¡Qué playas más (tan) bonitas! **d.** ¡Qué coches más (tan) rápidos!

❻ a. ¡Qué cansado parece este niño! **b.** ¡Qué cansado estoy! **c.** ¡Qué aspecto más cansado tienes! **d.** ¡Qué perro más listo tiene Miguel! **e.** ¡Qué cosas más divertidas cuentan mis amigos! **f.** ¡Qué libros más interesantes escribe usted! **g.** ¡Qué tarde comen los españoles!

❼ a. José tiene cuarenta y cinco años, Pedro cincuenta y Juan treinta y ocho: José es <u>mayor</u> que Juan y <u>menor</u> que Pedro. **b.** Vivir en una ciudad es <u>mejor</u> para las diversiones pero el aire es de <u>peor</u> calidad que en el campo.

❽ a. Conozco menos ciudades que tú. **b.** Tengo más libros que él. **c.** La cerveza es tan cara como en Inglaterra. **d.** Trabajo tantas horas como tú. **e.** Trabaja tanto como yo. **f.** Son tan altos como tontos.

Vocabulary and comprehension 1: identity & family

❶ [4] Soy de Madrid. [5] ¿A qué te dedicas? [1] Hola, me llamo Ana, ¿y tú, cómo te llamas? [3] Encantada. Soy argentina. Y tú, ¿de dónde eres? [6] Trabajo en un hospital, soy enfermero. [2] Hola, yo soy Luis. Encantado.

❷ ¿Cómo se llama el fotógrafo? → Se llama Ángel Ruiz Pellicer. / ¿A qué se dedica Rosana Bisbal Antón? → Es comercial. / ¿Dónde vive la abogada? → Vive en Acapulco. / ¿Cuál es el número de teléfono del periodista? → Es el 933547677.

❸ a. ¿Cómo se llama el periodista? **b.** ¿A qué se dedica Ángel Ruiz Pellicer? **c.** ¿Dónde vive Rosana Bisbal Antón? **d.** ¿Cuál es el número de teléfono de la abogada?

❹ a. 274 de cada mil mujeres **b.** 7 de cada cien residentes **c.** Uno de cada diez hombres **d.** Tres de cada cuatro mujeres

❺ a. Verdadero **b.** Falso **c.** Verdadero **d.** Verdadero **e.** Falso **f.** Falso.

❻

	1900 1910	1910 1920	1930 1940	1940 1950	1950 1960	1960 1970	1970 1980	1980 1990	1990 2000	2000 ....
Adrián									X	X
Alejandro										X
José Antonio				X	X					
Daniel									X	X
David							X	X	X	
José	X	X	X	X						
Pablo									X	X

7 a. El siglo xxi. b. Comienzos del siglo xx. c. Finales de los años treinta. d. Hasta finales de los años cincuenta. e. A partir de comienzos de los años ochenta. f. El siglo xx.

8 From left to right and from bottom to top: José, Carmen / Javier, María, Julia, Lorenzo, Antonio, Rocío / Dolores, Andrés, Lucía, Paula, Juan, Luisa.

7. Verb phrases & more present tense irregularities

1 a. Vuelve a llamar a su hijo. b. Volvéis a contar la misma historia. c. El niño vuelve a mentir. d. Vuelvo a nacer. e. Vuelven a cerrar la puerta. f. Volvemos a estar juntos. g. Vuelven a trabajar en Madrid. h. Usted vuelve a viajar a España. i. Volvemos a ser amigos. j. Volvemos a leer este libro.

2 a. Mi abuelo suele acordarse de mí. b. Suelo conducir una moto. c. Sueles perder tus llaves. d. Suelo sentarme en este banco. e. Solemos hacer deporte. f. Usted suele entender rápido. g. Soléis hablar inglés. h. Sueles comer a las tres. i. ¿Sueles salir a bailar? j. Solemos estar en casa.

3 Ríes, reímos, ~~rein~~, reís, ~~riemos~~, río, ríen, ~~reo~~, ~~reí~~, ~~riéis~~, ríe, ~~rees~~. Present indicative of reír: río, ríes, ríe, reímos, reís, ríen.

4 a. ¿Por qué sonreís? ¿Pensáis en algo divertido? b. Tú, ¿cómo te despides de la gente: das un beso o das la mano? c. Mi hermano mide un metro noventa. d. Nosotros siempre vestimos pantalones vaqueros. e. Los niños siempre piden dinero a los padres. f. Camarero, ¿me sirve usted una cerveza, por favor? g. Si no repito muchas veces la conjugación, no me acuerdo.

5 a. Sirvo. b. Repetimos. c. Pides. d. Se despide. e. Miden. f. Usted ríe, señor. g. Sonreís, amigos míos. h. Visto.

6 a. ¿Qué estás diciendo? b. ¿Por qué está usted sonriendo? c. Mis hermanas se están vistiendo. d. No estamos pidiendo nada. e. Estoy repitiendo la lección. f. No estáis midiendo bien. g. Se está despidiendo de la abuela.

7 a. Entre París y Londres yo elijo París. b. ¿Seguís o abandonáis la carrera? c. Usted elige muy bien los colores con que viste. d. Estoy cansado: no sigo. e. Entre carne y pescado, nosotros elegimos pescado. f. Es un perro fiel: siempre sigue a su amo. g. Los gatos son independientes: no siguen a nadie. h. Eliges a tus amigos pero no a tus familiares.

8 a. Sigo escribiendo a mano. b. Siguen existiendo personas sin ordenador. c. Mi vieja pluma sigue sirviendo. d. Y tú, ¿sigues usando pluma y papel? e. Usted sigue haciendo las cosas como antes. f. Seguís siendo fieles al pasado. g. Seguimos sonriendo con las películas de Charlie Chaplin.

8. The present subjunctive

1 1st line: cantar, cante, cantes, cante, cantemos, cantéis, canten. 2nd line: escribir, escriba, escribas, escriba, escribamos, escribáis, escriban. 3rd line: salir, salga, salgas, salga, salgamos, salgáis, salgan. 4th line: vestir, vista, vistas, vista, vistamos, vistáis, vistan. 5th line: pensar, piense, pienses, piense, pensemos, penséis, piensen 6th line: leer, lea, leas, lea, leamos, leáis, lean. 7th line: conocer, conozca, conozcas, conozca, conozcamos, conozcáis, conozcan.

2 a. Hola, abuela, este libro es para ti, para que lo leas pensando en mí. b. Quiero que vosotros le escribáis una bonita carta a la abuela. c. A la abuela no le gusta Mario: no quiere que su nieta salga con él. d. La abuela quiere que nosotros vistamos bien para su cumpleaños. e. Queremos que usted también conozca a la abuela. f. La abuela me llama muy a menudo para que siempre piense en ella. g. La abuela quiere que sus nietos le canten la canción del cumpleaños feliz.

3 Queridos Reyes Magos: Soy un niño bueno y obediente que quiere mucho a sus padres. Por eso quiero que me traigáis un tren eléctrico muy grande, con muchos vagones para que pueda jugar con todos mis amigos. Ah, si es posible, también quiero que vengáis antes del 6 de enero porque el 8 vuelvo al cole y mis padres no quieren que juegue cuando hay escuela. ¡Muchas gracias! Manolito.

4 1st column: traer, traiga, traigas, traiga, traigamos, traigáis, traigan. 2nd column: poder, pueda, puedas, pueda, podamos, podáis, puedan. 3rd column: venir, venga, vengas, venga, vengamos, vengáis, vengan. 4th column: jugar, juegue, juegues, juegue, juguemos, juguéis, jueguen.

5 a. ¡Que viváis felices! b. ¡Que bailéis bien! c. ¡Que te diviertas! d. ¡Que vuelvas pronto!

6 a. ¡Ojalá tengan un buen viaje! b. ¡Ojalá viva usted muchos años! c. ¡Ojalá pueda asistir a tu cumpleaños! d. ¡Ojalá os guste esta paella! e. ¡Ojalá entiendas el problema! f. ¡Ojalá volvamos a España! g. ¡Ojalá los Reyes Magos traigan muchos regalos! h. ¡Ojalá sigas teniendo suerte!

7 a. No hablamos inglés. Qué lástima que no hablemos inglés. b. No bebéis cerveza. Qué lástima que no bebáis cerveza. c. No me gusta bailar. Qué lástima que no me guste bailar. d. No bailas bien. Qué lástima que no bailes bien. e. No conocen a mi hermana. Qué lástima que no conozcan a mi hermana. f. No oyes bien. Qué lástima que no oigas bien. g. No sirvo para nada. Qué lástima que no sirva para nada. h. No sonríen nunca. Qué lástima que no sonrían nunca.

8 a. usted / ¡No hagas eso! b. usted / ¡No comas paella! c. usted / ¡No leáis ese libro! d. tú / ¡No cierre la puerta! e. tú / ¡No se sienten aquí! f. usted / ¡No conduzcáis tan rápido! g. tú / ¡No digan palabrotas! h. tú / ¡No repita esa palabra!

9 a. Tal vez no abran por la tarde. b. Tal vez no comprenda el español. c. Tal vez no escribáis nunca cartas. d. Tal vez no hagas bien tu trabajo. e. Tal vez no lo reconozcamos. f. Tal vez no me despida de ellos. g. Tal vez no me entienda usted. h. Tal vez no os acordéis de él.

9. More on irregular conjugations & the subjunctive

1 a. ir: subjunctive b. caber: indicative c. saber: indicative d. saber: subjunctive e. dar: indicative f. oír: indicative g. ir: indicative h. ver: indicative i. ver: subjunctive j. ser: subjunctive k. estar: subjunctive

U	V	E	E	I	S	A	E
L	V	A	Y	A	M	O	S
C	A	B	E	N	U	I	T
O	I	T	O	M	S	S	É
I	S	Y	V	U	E	T	I
G	V	S	E	P	Á	I	S
O	E	I	A	R	I	S	O
D	O	Y	N	O	S	T	I

2 a. Este coche es muy espacioso: caben hasta seis personas. b. ¿Por qué vais siempre a Marbella? ¿Os gusta tanto la playa? c. Quiero que estéis en casa estudiando este fin de semana. d. Tal vez vayamos a Sevilla estas vacaciones. e. No sé dónde está esa calle, quizás lo sepáis vosotros. f. ¿Por qué no me ayudáis? No seáis tan perezosos. g. ¡Ojalá lo vean mis ojos. h. Habla más alto, no te oigo bien. i. No te veo, ¿dónde estás? j. Te doy un libro para tu hermano.

3 a. Sois auténticos españoles: dormís la siesta por la tarde. b. Cuando su hijo le miente, el padre está furioso. c. Si hace mal tiempo, tal vez prefiramos quedarnos en casa. d. Estamos acostumbrados al frío: no lo sentimos. e. Qué pena que los toros mueran durante las corridas. f. Ojalá os divirtáis mucho durante la fiesta. g. No nos gusta ver películas en casa: preferimos salir. h. Siempre estáis de mal humor: no os divertís con nada. i. El padre no quiere que su hijo le mienta. j. Pone el radiador para que no sintamos frío. k. Ojalá durmáis bien esta noche. l. Algunas veces son los matadores los que mueren.

4 Free response.

5 a. No creo que la tecnología haga más felices a los hombres. / ¡No creo que Internet aísle completamente a la gente! b. No pienso que los jóvenes de hoy solo piensen en su móvil. / ¡No pienso que muchos chicos y chicas colaboren en ONG's! c. No estoy convencido de que vivamos en un mundo que progresa sin cesar. / ¡No estoy convencido de que miles de personas mueran de hambre cada día! d. No estoy seguro de que entender de informática ayude a conseguir un trabajo. / ¡No estoy seguro de que lo más importante sea tener una bonita letra! e. No es verdad que hoy la inmensa mayoría de la gente tenga un ordenador. / ¡No es verdad que en muchos países el ordenador siga siendo un lujo!

6 a. Me pregunto dónde vive. b. No sé por qué bebe. c. Creo que tienen dos hijos. d. Me parece que no trabajas. e. ¿Piensas que está enfermo?

7 **a.** Me pides que te ayude. **b.** Te pido que salgas. **c.** Nos pide que repitamos. **d.** Nos pide que abramos. **e.** Usted me pide que cante.

8 **a.** *The teacher tells us to read the books in Spanish.* **b.** *The teacher tells us that we read very well.* **c.** *The teacher tells us that we are going to see a film.* **d.** *The teacher tells us to go and see films.*

9 **a.** La madre le dice a su hijo que <u>sea</u> prudente con la moto. **b.** Le pide que no <u>vaya</u> muy rápido. **c.** El hijo le dice que no <u>se preocupe</u>. **d.** Le dice que él <u>conduce</u> siempre con prudencia. **e.** Le dice a su madre que <u>duerma</u> tranquila. **f.** Le dice que <u>puede</u> dormir tranquila.

10. Expressing obligation or need & making commands

1 **a.** Necesita un ordenador. **b.** ¿Me necesitas? **c.** No te necesito. **d.** ¿Necesita dinero, señor? **e.** Necesitamos a Carmen. **f.** Hace falta un ordenador para trabajar. **g.** ¿Hacen falta gafas de sol? **h.** Hacen falta gambas en la paella. **i.** Para hacer una tortilla, hacen falta huevos. **j.** ¿Hace falta pan?

2 **a.** <u>¿Hay que</u> sentarse aquí? *Do we have to sit here?* **b.** <u>¿Hace falta que</u> compremos pan? *Do we need to buy bread?* **c.** <u>¿Hace falta que</u> venga Pedro? *Does Pedro have to come?* **d.** No <u>hay que</u> mentir. *You mustn't lie.* **e.** <u>Hay que</u> cerrar la puerta. *We need to close the door.* **f.** <u>Hace falta que</u> vuelvas. *You need to return.* **g.** <u>Hay que</u> viajar a menudo. *One has to travel often.* **h.** <u>Hay que</u> leer libros. *It is necessary to read books.* **i.** <u>Hace falta que</u> lo sepas. *You need to know.*

3 **a.** Hace falta que hablen con él. **b.** Hace falta que leamos este libro. **c.** Hace falta que seáis pacientes. **d.** Hace falta que sigas estudiando.

4 **a.** Tienes que hacer un esfuerzo. **b.** No tenéis que pedir ayuda. **c.** ¿Tengo que ir yo? **d.** Tenemos que estar tranquilos.

5
infinitive	hablar	decir	hacer	pedir	ir	cerrar
tú	habla	di	haz	pide	ve	cierra
vosotros	hablad	decid	haced	pedid	id	cerrad

6 **a.** No os oigo: ¡<u>hablad</u> un poco más alto, por favor! **b.** ¡<u>Di</u> la verdad! ¿Me quieres o no? **c.** ¡Niños, antes de jugar, <u>haced</u> los deberes para la escuela! **d.** Isabel, ¡<u>ve</u> a comprar el pan, por favor! **e.** ¡<u>Cerrad</u> bien la puerta! Os lo pido por favor. **f.** Hoy es tu cumpleaños: <u>pide</u> lo que quieres comer.

7 **a.** Contádsela. **b.** Llámalo. **c.** Póntela. **d.** Escribidlos. **e.** Probadlas. **f.** Dáselo. **g.** Entiéndela. **h.** Conducidlo.

8 **a.** Acuérdate de mí. **b.** Acordaos de él. **c.** Divertíos mucho. **d.** Diviértete en esa fiesta.

9 **a.** Informal **b.** Formal **c.** Formal **d.** Informal.

10 **a.** Haz deporte. **b.** Haced deporte. **c.** Haga deporte. **d.** Hagan deporte. **e.** Ten cuidado con el perro. **f.** Tened cuidado con el perro. **g.** Tenga cuidado con el perro. **h.** Tengan cuidado con el perro. **i.** Conduce lentamente. **j.** Conducid lentamente. **k.** Conduzca lentamente. **l.** Conduzcan lentamente. **m.** Ponte el cinturón. **n.** Poneos el cinturón. **o.** Póngase el cinturón. **p.** Pónganse el cinturón.

11. More on adjectives, adverbs & prepositions

1 **a.** Es un río <u>larguísimo</u>. **b.** Hay <u>muchísimos</u> tipos de peces. **c.** Quedan <u>poquísimas</u> tribus primitivas. **d.** Es <u>riquísima</u> en recursos naturales. **e.** Es <u>peligrosísima</u> para el planeta. **f.** Es <u>importantísimo</u> proteger Amazonia.

2 **a.** Es la ciudad más poblada del mundo. **b.** Es el río más largo del mundo. **c.** Es el pájaro más ligero del mundo. **d.** Son los animales más longevos del mundo.

3 **a.** Me gusta <u>mucho</u> chatear en Internet. **b.** Me hago <u>muchos</u> amigos chateando. **c.** Me paso <u>muchas</u> horas conectado. **d.** Para los niños, Internet puede ser <u>muy</u> peligroso. **e.** Hay <u>mucha</u> información interesante en línea. **f.** Suelo perder <u>mucho</u> tiempo en Internet. **g.** <u>Muchos</u> chicos juegan en línea. **h.** El juego en línea provoca <u>mucha</u> adicción.

4 **a.** Hago poco deporte. **b.** Comes poco pescado. **c.** Son poco simpáticos. **d.** Somos poco pacientes. **e.** Compro pocos zapatos. **f.** Come poca carne. **g.** Escribes pocas cartas. **h.** Esta película es poco interesante.

5 **a.** ¡Juegas <u>demasiado</u> a la Play Station! **b.** ¡Te pasas <u>demasiadas</u> horas en Internet! **c.** ¡Te acuestas <u>demasiado</u> tarde! **d.** ¡Tienes <u>demasiados</u> amigos! **e.** ¡Soy <u>demasiado</u> paciente contigo! **f.** ¡Tienes <u>demasiada</u> libertad!

6 **a.** ¡Mentira! Mis notas son <u>bastante</u> buenas. **b.** ¡Mentira! No tengo <u>bastantes</u> amigos. **c.** ¡Mentira! No eres <u>bastante</u> paciente conmigo. **d.** ¡Mentira! No tengo <u>bastante</u> libertad.

7
cariñoso	cariñosa	cariñosamente
ágil	ágil	ágilmente
triste	triste	tristemente
feroz	feroz	ferozmente
cómodo	cómoda	cómodamente
único	única	únicamente

a. Este perro es muy malo: ladra <u>ferozmente</u> a todos los que pasan. **b.** El perro está malo: me mira <u>tristemente</u>. **c.** El gato duerme <u>cómodamente</u> en el sofá. **d.** El gato salta <u>ágilmente</u> por la ventana. **e.** A los gatos les gusta que les acaricien <u>cariñosamente</u>. **f.** Las jirafas viven <u>únicamente</u> en África.

8 **a.** <u>Es esencial</u> estudiar los verbos. **b.** <u>Está prohibido</u> fumar en este bar. **c.** Esta palabra es <u>imposible de</u> pronunciar. **d.** A mí me <u>es fácil</u> aprender idiomas. **e.** No <u>es fácil</u> recordar las conjugaciones.

9 **a.** <u>En</u> Sevilla, la gente es muy simpática. **b.** Los estudiantes que residen <u>en</u> Sevilla están muy contentos. **c.** Muchos alumnos van <u>a</u> Sevilla para estudiar. **d.** Cuando vuelven <u>a</u> su país, sienten nostalgia. **e.** ¿Dónde estás? <u>¿En</u> casa? **f.** Ven <u>a</u> casa, te invito.

Vocabulary and comprehension 2: getting around

1 **a.** ida **b.** llegada **c.** billete **d.** fecha **e.** salida **f.** metálico **g.** gastos **h.** plaza **i.** precio **j.** vuelta **k.** reserva **l.** tarifa **m.** tren **n.** IVA **o.** coche.

2 **a.** Tres. **b.** Lo habla pero bastante mal. **c.** Frank quiere un billete de tren para París. **d.** El empleado de la taquilla no entiende bien a Frank.

3 **a.** El empleado no es sordo. **b.** Hay que hablar despacio. **c.** Veo a alguien detrás de Frank.

4 **a.** Hola, ¿vende usted <u>billetes</u> para trenes de cercanías? **b.** Cómprame dos <u>entradas</u> para el concierto de Bisbal, por favor. **c.** El <u>billete</u> de autobús es más barato que el de tren. **d.** En avión, si tienes <u>billete</u> de primera clase, ¡te dan champán gratis! **e.** Las <u>entradas</u> para las corridas de toros suelen ser bastante caras. **f.** Para esta obra de teatro, puedes comprar <u>entradas</u> en Internet.

5 **a.** Este joven <u>oye</u> muy bien: no hace falta que hable tan alto. **b.** Leo bien el español pero no <u>entiendo</u> a la gente cuando habla demasiado rápido. **c.** Sube el volumen de la música, por favor: ¡no <u>oigo</u> nada! **d.** Este texto es demasiado difícil para mí: no <u>entiendo</u> nada. **e.** ¿<u>Entiende</u> usted lo que digo o se lo vuelvo a explicar? **f.** ¡Estoy en el tren! Hay mucho ruido. ¿Me <u>oyes</u>?

6 **a.** puerta **b.** llave **c.** sobrinos **d.** aquí **e.** precio **f.** silla **g.** perra **h.** fin **i.** Quisiera un billete sencillo para París, por favor. **j.** *I'd like a single/one-way ticket to Paris, please.*

7 **a.** Tratamiento de tú **b.** Tratamiento de usted **c.** Tratamiento de usted **d.** Tratamiento de tú.

8 **a.** El colegio está en la calle Mayor. **b.** La biblioteca está en la calle San Miguel. **c.** La discoteca está en el Paseo de la Paz. **d.** El cine está en la calle Real.

9 Examples of possible answers:

– Por favor, ¿dónde está la biblioteca?

– Tienes que tomar la calle Real, seguir todo recto, tomar la segunda calle a la derecha y luego la primera a la izquierda: es allí.

– Toma la primera a la derecha, luego gira por la primera a la izquierda y sigue todo recto.

12. The future & relative clauses

1 **a.** future: haré / infinitive: hacer **b.** future: regalaré / infinitive: regalar **c.** future: serás / infinitive: ser **d.** future: harás / infinitive: hacer **e.** future: ganarás / infinitive: ganar **f.** future: seducirás / infinitive: seducir **g.** future: tendrás / infinitive: tener.

2 **a.** haré, harás, hará, haremos, haréis, harán. **b.** regalaré, regalarás, regalará, regalaremos, regalaréis, regalarán.

3 **a.** ¿Me ayudarás a tocar la guitarra? **b.** Seremos famosos. **c.** No podré tocar esta partitura. **d.** Me diréis qué os parece esta guitarra. **e.** El público querrá que sigas tocando. **f.** No tendrán tiempo para aprender.

4 **a.** Me pregunto si vendrán. **b.** En cuanto te vea, te pagaré. **c.** No sabe si podrá venir. **d.** ¿Sabes cuándo saldrá su libro? **e.** Se pregunta dónde vivirá. **f.** El día que te pague, estarás contento. **g.** No sé cómo vestiré. **h.** No sé si cantaremos. **i.** Leeré su libro cuando salga. **j.** Mientras haga sol, iré a la playa.

5 **a.** Cuando <u>hable bien</u> español, <u>iré</u> a México. **b.** Cuando <u>sea</u> mayor de edad, <u>conduciré</u> una moto. **c.** Cuando las <u>aprendas</u>, <u>sabrás</u> las conjugaciones. **d.** Cuando <u>estudie</u>, este chico <u>tendrá</u> buenas notas. **e.** Cuando <u>haga</u> sol, <u>irán</u> a la playa.

6 **a.** *The person you are looking for does not live here: there must be a mistake.* **b.** *Pedro has called ten times: he must want to tell you something important.*

7 **a.** <u>Quizás esté repasando</u> un examen. **b.** <u>Estará repasando</u> un examen. **c.** <u>A lo mejor no tiene cobertura</u> el móvil. **d.** <u>No tendrá cobertura</u> el móvil. **e.** <u>Quizás vaya</u> al gimnasio. **f.** <u>A lo mejor va</u> al gimnasio.

8 **a.** <u>La mujer a quien (a la que, a la cual) me dirijo</u> es mi profesora. **b.** <u>El barrio en el que vivo</u> es muy simpático. **c.** <u>La moto con la que (con la cual) reparto pizzas</u> es verde. **d.** <u>La chica de quien (de la que, de la cual) te hablo</u> es mi vecina.

9 **a.** La ciudad <u>donde / en que</u> se pasan las vacaciones está a la orilla del mar. **b.** Me acuerdo muy bien de la noche <u>en que</u> te conocí. **c.** ¿Cuál fue el año <u>en que</u> el Barça ganó la Champions? **d.** Esta es la casa <u>donde / en que</u> me gustaría vivir.

10 **a.** Ven cuando <u>puedas</u>. *Come when you can.* **b.** El primero que <u>llame</u> tendrá un coche. *The first one who calls me will get a car.* **c.** El día que <u>vengas</u>, estaré contento. *The day you come, I'll be happy.* **d.** Querré al hombre que me <u>entienda</u>. *I'll love the man who understands me.*

13. Talking about the past

1 **1st line:** jugar, jugaba, jugabas, jugaba, jugábamos, jugabais, jugaban. **2nd line:** estar, estaba, estabas, estaba, estábamos, estabais, estaban. **3rd line:** hacer, hacía, hacías, hacía, hacíamos, hacíais, hacían. **4th line:** decir, decía, decías, decía, decíamos, decíais, decían. **5th line:** divertirse, me divertía, te divertías, se divertía, nos divertíamos, os divertíais, se divertían.

2 **a.** En mi época, yo no <u>iba</u> tanto al cine. **b.** Cuando <u>tenía</u> quince años, yo no <u>era</u> tan libre. **c.** Cuando <u>éramos</u> pequeños, nosotros no <u>veíamos</u> tanto la tele. **d.** Los mayores oían la radio y los niños <u>jugaban</u> en la calle.

3 Toda la familia <u>estaba</u> en el salón: <u>era</u> la hora de la comida y todos <u>estaban</u> viendo la tele. A veces, los padres y los hijos no <u>estaban</u> de acuerdo: unos <u>eran</u> partidarios de ver las series y otros <u>estaban</u> a favor del telediario. Pero el padre siempre <u>estaba</u> de mal humor y además <u>era</u> muy autoritario, de modo que siempre <u>era</u> él quien decidía.

4 pagué, ~~escribe~~, contó, cerró, contamos, cerraron, escribimos, bebí, ~~bebemos~~, ~~contéis~~, ~~juegue~~, escribiste, pagasteis, ~~cierro~~, bebió.

5 **a.** bailar: bailé, bailaste, bailó, bailamos, bailasteis, bailaron. **b.** pensar: pensé, pensaste, pensó, pensamos, pensasteis, pensaron. **c.** volver: volví, volviste, volvió, volvimos, volvisteis, volvieron.

V	T	L	E	Ó	N	T	E
T	O	M	I	E	R	O	N
B	A	L	P	E	N	S	É
A	M	I	V	U	A	S	O
I	I	L	I	L	E	T	E
L	C	Y	V	G	S	U	R
I	H	C	I	U	R	T	U
Ó	U	T	Ó	É	L	L	E

6 **a.** El año pasado no <u>ayudaste</u> en casa, pero este año vas a ayudar. **b.** El curso pasado no <u>leí</u> pero este año voy a leer. **c.** El año pasado <u>perdisteis</u> mucho tiempo en Internet, pero este año no vais a perder tanto. **d.** El año pasado mi hermano <u>jugó</u> mucho al fútbol, pero este año no va a jugar tanto.

7 **a.** no saber la respuesta → no escribir nada **b.** la puerta / estar cerrada → entrar por la ventana **c.** no quedar café → preparar un té **d.** María / no contestar al teléfono → llamar a su puerta **e.** no haber billetes de avión → viajar en tren **f.** no tener ganas de salir → decidir ver una serie en la tele **g.** el ascensor / no funcionar → subir por las escaleras **h.** el título/ parecer interesante → abrir el libro **i.** yo / querer trabajar en Madrid → aprender español **j.** el programa / no ser interesante → apagar la tele

8 **a.** Como no <u>sabía</u> la respuesta, no <u>escribí</u> nada. **b.** Como la puerta <u>estaba</u> cerrada, <u>entré</u> por la ventana. **c.** Como no <u>quedaba</u> café, <u>preparé</u> un té. **d.** Como María no <u>contestaba</u> al teléfono, <u>llamé</u> a su puerta. **e.** Como no <u>había</u> billetes de avión, <u>viajé</u> en tren. **f.** Como no <u>tenía</u> ganas de salir, <u>decidí</u> ver una serie en la tele. **g.** Como el ascensor no <u>funcionaba</u>, <u>subí</u> por las escaleras. **h.** Como el título <u>parecía</u> interesante, <u>abrí</u> el libro. **i.** Como <u>quería</u> trabajar en Madrid, <u>aprendí</u> español. **j.** Como el programa no <u>era</u> interesante, <u>apagué</u> la tele.

9 **a.** Yo no he abierto la puerta. **b.** Habéis vuelto de las vacaciones cansados. **c.** ¿Le has escrito a la abuela? **d.** No hemos podido venir a tu cumpleaños. **e.** ¿Ustedes han pedido pescado?

10 **a.** No encuentro las llaves: ¿dónde las <u>habéis puesto</u>? **b.** No estoy contento contigo: no <u>has hecho</u> tus deberes. **c.** ¿Quién <u>ha visto</u> mis gafas? **d.** Te <u>he dicho</u> mil veces que no te pases horas con el ordenador. **e.** Muchas gracias por la invitación: <u>hemos comido</u> muy bien. **f.** Te <u>han llamado</u> Carmen y Juan.

11 **a.** Ya (*or* todavía no) he viajado en avión. **b.** Ya (*or* todavía no) he comido paella. **c.** Ya (*or* todavía no) he visto una película española en VO. **d.** Ya (*or* todavía no) he hecho autoestop. **e.** Ya (*or* todavía no) he cantado flamenco. **f.** Ya (*or* todavía no) he tenido un diario íntimo. **g.** Ya (*or* todavía no) he estado enamorado/-a. **h.** Ya (*or* todavía no) me he bañado en el Atlántico. **i.** Ya (*or* todavía no) he hecho un discurso. **j.** Ya (*or* todavía no) he subido en globo. **k.** Ya (*or* todavía no) he actuado en una obra teatral. **l.** Ya (*or* todavía no) he ido a América latina.

14. More about tenses

1 **a.** A los diez años <u>tuve</u> mi primera bicicleta. **b.** Eres una mentirosa: ¿por qué no me <u>dijiste</u> la verdad? **c.** ¿Por qué no <u>vinisteis</u> a mi cumpleaños? **d.** Ayer <u>hizo</u> bastante sol. **e.** Había demasiada gente y no <u>pudieron</u> entrar en el estadio. **f.** La semana pasada <u>fuimos</u> a ver a la abuela.

V	I	N	I	S	T	E	I	S
P	H	I	L	T	O	R	F	A
T	U	P	B	R	A	Z	Y	T
T	E	D	I	J	I	S	T	E
O	B	L	I	L	C	H	U	S
H	R	U	T	E	S	O	V	I
I	M	A	L	L	R	H	E	J
Z	U	F	U	I	M	O	S	T
O	Q	U	O	T	N	A	N	I

2 **a.** Cristóbal Colón descubrió América pero no fue él quien le dio su nombre al Nuevo Mundo. **b.** Midió mal la circunferencia de la Tierra, por eso el viaje duró más de lo previsto. **c.** Repitió el viaje a América cuatro veces y murió en Valladolid. **d.** Los españoles introdujeron nuevas enfermedades en América. **e.** Destruyeron las antiguas culturas precolombinas y construyeron otra civilización.

3 **a.** <u>Cuando abrí el periódico</u>, fui directamente a la página de deportes. **b.** <u>Cuando llegué a México</u>, noté que el acento era diferente del de España. **c.** <u>Cuando vimos que no hacía sol</u>, decidimos quedarnos en casa.

4 **a.** <u>Al volver a casa</u>, el padre vio que su hijo estaba escuchando música. **b.** <u>Al oír ruido</u>, miraron por la ventana. **c.** <u>Al morir</u>, dejó todo su dinero a una ONG.

5 **a.** Preterite **b.** Present perfect **c.** Near future **d.** Future.

6 **a.** Antes de ayer, Belén <u>comió con don Andrés y fue al cine con Pepa y Emilia</u>. **b.** Ayer, Belén <u>trajo los periódicos a la tienda y escribió a Carlota</u>. **c.** Esta mañana, Belén <u>ha ido al médico y esta tarde va a despedirse de Pedro</u>. **d.** Mañana, Belén <u>dará un</u>

paseo en bici con Isa y pondrá en el facebook las recomendaciones del librero. **e.** Pasado mañana, Belén hará la mochila de Isa para la excursión y saldrá con Juan Carlos.

7 **a.** ¿Podría utilizar tu móvil? **b.** ¿Sería posible vernos más tarde? **c.** Desearíamos un móvil más barato. **d.** ¿Estaríais dispuestos a ayudarnos? **e.** ¿Me harías un favor? **f.** ¿Me dirías la respuesta?

8 **a.** Estos niños pensaban que de mayores serían futbolistas. **b.** ¿Te imaginabas que un día tendrías nietos? **c.** El profesor decía que pronto sabríamos hablar español. **d.** Mi abuelo creía que los extraterrestres nos invadirían. **e.** Estaba convencido de que me haría este favor.

15. Tense sequence & conditions

1

Preterite			Imperfect subjunctive		
pedir	leer	tener	pedir	leer	tener
pedí	leí	tuve	pidiera	leyera	tuviera
pediste	leíste	tuviste	pidieras	leyeras	tuvieras
pidió	leyó	tuvo	pidiera	leyera	tuviera
pedimos	leímos	tuvimos	pidiéramos	leyéramos	tuviéramos
pedisteis	leísteis	tuvisteis	pidierais	leyerais	tuvierais
pidieron	leyeron	tuvieron	pidieran	leyeran	tuvieran

2 **a.** Te llamo para que vengas a ayudarme. **b.** Quiero que alguien me diga cómo usar este programa. **c.** Le pido al servicio técnico que me explique lo que pasa. **d.** Me dicen que ojalá sea solo un problema material. **e.** Yo les digo que tal vez tenga algún virus el ordenador.

3 **a.** No hacía falta que compraras el pan. **b.** Te di dinero para que fueras a hacer la compra. **c.** No quería que volvieras a traer chorizo. **d.** No creía que necesitáramos más vino. **e.** Te pedí sobre todo que pensaras en el chocolate.

4 **a.** Hago como si me gustara el cine. **b.** Hizo como si se acordara de mí. **c.** Hacen como si durmieran. **d.** Hace como si supiera la respuesta.

5 **Imperfect subjunctive:** pusieran, hiciera, condujeras, oyeras. **Conditional:** habría, iríamos, costaría, encantaría.

6 **a.** Si todos se pusieran el cinturón de seguridad, habría menos accidentes graves. **b.** Si hiciera mejor tiempo, iríamos a la playa. **c.** Si condujeras más despacio, el coche te costaría menos en gasolina. **d.** Si oyeras cómo toca la guitarra, te encantaría.

7 **a.** No es mayor de edad. Hace como si fuera mayor de edad. **b.** Si Pedro estuviera aquí, nos ayudaría. **c.** No duerme, hace como si estuviera durmiendo. **d.** Si no estuviera tan cansado, te acompañaría. **e.** Si estuviera de mejor humor, iría al cine. **f.** ¡Aprender chino! Como si fuera tan fácil.

8 **a.** Si estuviera enfermo, iría al médico. **b.** Si supiera de informática, no tendría tantos problemas con el ordenador. **c.** Si tuviera tu número de móvil, te mandaría mensajes. **d.** Si visitara México, subiría a las pirámides. **e.** Si viviera en Argentina, cruzaría la Pampa a caballo. **f.** Si durmiera más, estaría más relajado.

9 **a.** Contrary-to-fact: Aunque tuviera tiempo, no te ayudaría. Translation: *Even if I had time, I wouldn't help you.* **b.** Contrary-to-fact: Aunque hiciera mal tiempo, iría a correr. Translation: *Even if the weather were bad, I would go for a run.* **c.** Contrary-to-fact: Aunque estuviera enfermo, trabajaría. Translation: *Even if I were ill, I would work.* **d.** Contrary-to-fact: Aunque vivieras cien años, no leerías todos los libros. Translation: *Even if you were to live for a hundred years, you wouldn't read every book.* **e.** Contrary-to-fact: Aunque escribieras veinte libros, no serías célebre. Translation: *Even if you were to write twenty books, you wouldn't be famous.*

10 **a.** Digas lo que digas, no te creeré. **b.** Vayas donde vayas, te seguiré. **c.** Sea cuando sea, esta tarde o esta noche, tengo que verte. **d.** Llame quien llame, no estoy. **e.** Bailes como bailes, bien o mal, me gusta bailar contigo.

11 **a.** Digan lo que digan mis amigos, lo haré. **b.** Venga quien venga a esta fiesta, yo no iré. **c.** Conduzca como conduzca, rápido o despacio, siempre tengo accidentes. **d.** Las ponga donde las ponga, siempre pierdo las llaves. **e.** Llames cuando llames, aunque sea tarde, te contestaré.

16. Compound tenses & auxiliary verbs

1 **a.** Passive voice **b.** Active voice **c.** Active voice **d.** Passive voice **e.** Passive voice **f.** Passive voice **g.** Active voice **h.** Passive voice.

2 **a.** El viento abrió la puerta. **b.** He sido invitado por mi primo para su cumpleaños. **c.** Estos cuadernos de ejercicios han sido escritos por Juan. **d.** Muchas personas utilizan estos cuadernos. **e.** El año que viene, Assimil publicará otro cuaderno. **f.** El público aprecia mucho a estos autores. **g.** Las personas que saben idiomas son contratadas por las empresas. **h.** Ojalá la empresa no despida a mis amigos.

3 **a.** Para llegar a casa, lo mejor es que pases por aquí. **b.** He reservado una mesa para cuatro personas. **c.** No me gusta trabajar por la noche. **d.** Viene a verme una vez por año. **e.** ¿Por dónde estará? Hace días que no lo veo. **f.** ¿Estás cansado? Esto te pasa por acostarte tan tarde. **g.** Por su capacidad, es un coche para familias numerosas. **h.** ¿Me podrías entregar el trabajo para el martes?

4 **a.** Para comer una buena paella, ve a este restaurante. **b.** He traído algo para ti. **c.** El deporte es bueno para la salud. **d.** He viajado por España este verano. **e.** Por la mañana, tomo café. **f.** Para ti, ¿cuál es la mejor película? **g.** Quiero este trabajo para mañana.

5 **a.** Juan se ha arruinado con el juego. **b.** Soy español, he nacido en Sevilla. **c.** Como la puerta estaba cerrada, he entrado por la ventana. **d.** Juan está insatisfecho con el resultado del partido. **e.** Yo he cerrado bien la puerta: ¿por qué está abierta? **f.** Como hacía buen tiempo, hemos salido a pasear. **g.** La empresa lo ha despedido: no tiene trabajo y está desesperado. **h.** ¡Si mis gafas están rotas es que alguien las ha roto!

6 **a.** Hemos subido para verte. **b.** Han vuelto para comprar el pan. **c.** Las puertas están bien cerradas. **d.** La puerta fue (or ha sido) abierta por el viento. **e.** Esta película fue (or ha sido) vista por muchas personas. **f.** He roto mis gafas. **g.** Mis gafas están rotas. **h.** Este libro está bien escrito.

7 **a.** Si fuera más alto, jugaría al baloncesto. **b.** Si mi móvil tuviera cobertura, te escribiría un mensaje. **c.** Si hiciera mal tiempo, me pondría la gabardina. **d.** Si supiera hablar español, haría un gran viaje por América latina. **e.** Si tuviera la llave, abriría la puerta.

8 **a.** Si hubiera sido más alto, hubiera (or habría) jugado al baloncesto. **b.** Si mi móvil hubiera tenido cobertura, te hubiera (or habría) escrito un mensaje. **c.** Si hubiera hecho mal tiempo, me hubiera (or habría) puesto la gabardina. **d.** Si hubiera sabido hablar español, hubiera (or habría) hecho un gran viaje por América latina. **e.** Si hubiera tenido la llave, hubiera (or habría) abierto la puerta.

9 **a.** Si no hubiera comprado este cuaderno, no habría repasado la gramática. **b.** No había hecho tantos ejercicios en mi vida. **c.** Cuando haya repasado toda la gramática, hablaré bastante mejor español. **d.** Siempre me ha encantado aprender idiomas.

Vocabulary and comprehension 3: clothing

1 D / C / A / E / B.

2 **a.** Los dos personajes de este diálogo son una madre y su hija. **b.** La joven que habla va a ir a una fiesta. **c.** Según ella, sus amigas van a vestir un top y una minifalda. **d.** No quiere ponerse las faldas que tiene porque no son de marca.

3 **a.** something ridiculous **b.** How silly! **c.** Well, I don't know … **d.** It's really cute.

4 **a.** Tu falda será de Primark pero es monísima. **b.** Todas mis amigas van de marca. **c.** Tu armario está lleno de vestidos y de minifaldas. **d.** Si no quiero ir vestida así a una fiesta. **e.** ¿Cómo puedes decir que no tienes nada que ponerte?

5 **a.** cazadora **b.** zapatos **c.** camisa **d.** vaqueros **e.** falda **f.** pantalón **g.** vestido **h.** chándal **i.** chaqueta.

6 **a.** paella **b.** suegra **c.** quince **d.** ese **e.** amistad **f.** horas **g.** usted **h.** oye **i.** Assimil espera que le haya gustado este cuaderno. **j.** *Assimil hopes that you have enjoyed this workbook!*

¡Excelente! You've reached the end of this workbook. Now it's time to assess how you did by counting up the icons of each type for all the lessons. Make sure that you've put the sub-totals from each lesson in the boxes below, and then add them up to find the total number for each of the three icons.

☺ ☻ ☹   ☺ ☻ ☹

1. Letters, sounds & punctuation......................

2. Articles, nouns, adjectives & numbers ....

3. Conjugation & personal pronouns...................

4. Possessives, demonstratives & indefinite pronouns......

5. *Ser, estar* & progressive tenses.....................

6. Present tense irregularities & simple sentences.........

Vocabulary and comprehension 1: identity & family.....

7. Verb phrases & more present tense irregularities.......

8. The present subjunctive................................

9. More on irregular conjugations & the subjunctive.........

10. Expressing obligation or need & making commands....

11. More on adjectives, adverbs & prepositions...............

Vocabulary and comprehension 2: getting around

12. The future & relative clauses ....

13. Talking about the past ....

14. More about tenses....................................

15. Tense sequence & conditions.........................

16. Compound sentences & auxiliary verbs ....

Vocabulary and comprehension 3: clothing ....

☺ ☻ ☹

Total (all lessons) ....

Which icon has the highest total?

¡Matrícula de honor! You have mastered the basics of Spanish and are ready to move on to the next level!

No está mal… but there is room for improvement. Go back and redo the exercises that gave you trouble, reviewing the information if necessary.

¡Ánimo! You're a bit rusty … Go through the workbook again and redo the exercises, reviewing the information first.

Credits: photos pp. 38 and 74 © MS / photo page 41 © Stock.xchng / Illustrations © MS

Designed by: MediaSarbacane
Layout: Violeta Cabal

© 2016 Assimil
Legal deposit: February 2016
Publication number: 3513
ISBN: 978-2-7005-0714-0
www.assimil.com
Printed in Slovenia by DZS Grafik